MARY, QUEEN OF SCOTS

The death of her young husband, Francis II, King of France, left Mary numb but determined. At eighteen she could not live out her life in exile. Queen of Scotland by birth, rightful heir to the throne of England, she must return home and claim her inheritance.

So began the years of conspiracy and intrigue, during which time Mary's hot passions and thirst for revenge overwhelmed all judgement, reason and honour ...

John Hale served in the Royal Navy before working in the theatre, television and films. He founded and directed the Lincoln Theatre Company in the mid-fifties before going on to be artistic director of the Bristol Old Vic. He directed plays in London, at the Edinburgh Festival, the Baalbek Festival and in America. As a freelance director he also worked in television.

He became a full-time writer in the mid-sixties and is the author of four novels: *Kissed The Girls And Made Them Cry*, *The Grudge Fight*, *A Fool At The Feast* and *The Paradise Man*. He is also the author of four stage plays, each of which he directed himself: *It's All In The Mind*, *The Black Swan Winter*, *Spithead* and *Lorna And Ted*. He was nominated for an 'Oscar' and won a Golden Globe award for his work on the screenplay of the Royal Command Film, *Anne Of A Thousand Days*. His most recent television play was *The Lion's Cub*, first in the *Elizabeth R* series.

THE FILM

MARY, QUEEN OF SCOTS is a Hal Wallis Production
for Universal Pictures

Producer: Hal B. Wallis   Director: Charles Jarrott
Original Screenplay by John Hale

Filmed in Panavision ® and Technicolor ®
Music by John Barry

Cast

MARY, QUEEN OF SCOTS	*Vanessa Redgrave*
ELIZABETH I OF ENGLAND	*Glenda Jackson*
JAMES STUART, EARL OF MORAY	*Patrick McGoohan*
LORD HENRY DARNLEY	*Timothy Dalton*
JAMES HEPBURN, EARL OF BOTHWELL	*Nigel Davenport*
WILLIAM CECIL, LORD BURGHLEY	*Trevor Howard*
DAVID RICCIO	*Ian Holm*
ROBERT DUDLEY, EARL OF LEICESTER	*Daniel Massey*
BALLARD	*Tom Fleming*
ANDREW	*Jeremy Bulloch*
MARY SETON	*Beth Harris*
MARY FLEMING	*Frances White*
LADY JEAN GORDON, COUNTESS OF BOTHWELL	*Maria Aitken*
KING FRANCIS II OF FRANCE	*Richard Denning*
DUC DE GUISE	*Vernon Dobtcheff*
CARDINAL DE GUISE	*Raf de la Torre*
QUEEN CATHERINE DE MEDICI	*Katherine Kath*
JOHN KNOX	*Robert James*
SIR FRANCIS WALSINGHAM	*Richard Warner*
LORD PATRICK RUTHVEN	*Andrew Keir*
EARL OF MORTON	*Bruce Purchase*
EARL OF HUNTLEY	*Brian Coburn*

Released in the UK by Rank Film Distributors

MARY,
QUEEN OF SCOTS

John Hale

*The book of the film
from an original
screenplay by John Hale*

UNABRIDGED

PAN BOOKS LTD : LONDON

First published 1972 by Pan Books Ltd,
33 Tothill Street London, S.W.1

ISBN 0 330 02940 1

© John Hale 1972

Printed and bound in England by
Hazell Watson & Viney Ltd,
Aylesbury, Bucks

CHAPTER ONE

They were playing truant. They crept along passageways and down staircases, dodging into dark corners to avoid the sleepy guards coming off duty at dawn. They came out of the château at a side door and crossed the lawns near the cages of the hunting leopards, expecting every minute to be challenged.

The dew in the water meadow soaked their feet and ankles as they ran hand in hand, laughing so much at their own daring that their lungs nearly burst. By the river they were hidden from view. They wandered happily along the bank until they came upon a boat with the oars left in it.

'Come on,' she said.

He smiled up at her and tugged her hand to pull her away.

She read his thoughts and said, 'You can do anything if you want to.'

'Can I?' he said, hesitantly.

She laughed out loud at his anxious face. She embraced him. She had to bend a little to do this because she was very tall. She kissed him gently on each cheek and whispered in his ear, 'There's nothing you cannot do. Come.'

They got into the boat and it rocked. With some difficulty they pushed off from the bank. He found that he could row a boat and was delighted.

'We must do this every day,' he said solemnly.

She smiled with the happiness and surprise of it all and said, 'You have only to order it and it will happen.'

He stopped rowing and the boat drifted with the water lopping against the bow.

'I am afraid of my mother. She would prevent it.'

* * *

A fat, expressionless woman walked slowly and purposefully towards the royal apartments in the château. Behind her hurried a dwarf dressed as a jester leading an ape by a chain.

In the bedchamber the four ladies heard the dwarf approaching and were uneasy. The doors opened and Catherine de Medici stood there ready to greet her son and daughter-in-law as she did every morning. She saw the empty bed with its covers still thrown back, and the women of the bedchamber bent in deep curtsies with their heads down so that they should not meet her eyes. Catherine showed no sign of the anger which seized her; but they knew because she spoke to them first in French, forgetting for an instant that none of them was fluent.

'Where are they? Where have they gone?'

None of the women answered. Catherine still controlled her anger. She pointed at Mary Seton and said in English, 'You, Seton, tell me at once. Where have they gone?'

Seton forced herself to look up into the bulging eyes.

'I promised not to say, madam. I dare not break my promise.'

Catherine's anger broke out as she shouted, 'Promised? How could you make a promise like that? The King has been ill. He is forbidden by his doctors to leave the château. It is very dangerous to his health. Answer me at once. Where have they gone? Where has Mary Stuart taken him?'

Seton lowered her eyes and shook her head. Catherine struck her so hard across the face that she sprawled backwards across the floor. The other women dared not move to help her.

'I promise you,' said Catherine, 'that you will all answer to me if any harm comes to him. Now you,' she pointed to Mary Fleming, 'get me a chair. I will remain here until they return.'

As Seton picked herself up from the floor the ape began to chatter and jump up and down. The dwarf laughed and shook his bells and the pair of them ran to Catherine and clutched at her skirts. She put her hand down to stroke the head of the ape. The women, hurrying to bring her a chair, shivered as they looked at that greasy face with its heavy lips and long sloping nose. There were stories of her conducting the Black Mass with Nostradamus, the astrologer. They were careful not to touch any part of her, or her clothing, when she sat.

The boat drifted. Mary plaited flowers she had picked on the bank into Francis' hair. The early sun warmed them as they listened to the peaceful sound of distant cocks crowing. She was so happy that it made her fear some disaster. As her fingers touched his forehead she remembered something and shivered.

At the tournament, one year ago, the high sun had gleamed on the small crown of France which topped the helm of the jousting armour of Henry the King – father of her young husband Francis, now leaning on the oars before her. Henry sat a great horse with golden fleurs-de-lis upon its blue saddle-cloth. He raised his lance to take Mary's scarf on its point from where she sat in her box above the arena. Francis, beside her, edged back to hide himself from his father. All around them the sound of the crowd, the vendors, the armourers, the arrogant riders filled the air. Over the pavilions the banners of the House of Guise and the royal houses of France and Scotland drooped in the hot air. To the anger of the English ambassador the arms of England were quartered upon those of France, defiantly proclaiming Mary Stuart's claim to the English throne. The trumpets sounded. The King and his opponent rode to their places on opposite sides, and at opposite ends, of the long wooden barrier dividing the lists.

In her box which faced Mary, Catherine the Queen leaned forward in the sunlight to watch them. In the shadows behind her stood a tall, grave creature in a strange gown. Mary, from where she sat, saw the Queen turn to speak to him. She could guess the question. Catherine asked it whenever there was possible danger to the King. Nostradamus had made a prophecy.

'Is this the day, Nostradamus?'

And on this day Nostradamus replied, 'It is, madam.'

'What do you see?'

'I see blood.'

'But whose blood – the King's or his opponent's?'

'I cannot tell.'

The trumpets sounded and the two great horses charged. The King splintered his lance on the shield of his opponent and unhorsed him. There was a great roar from the crowd. Catherine leaned back with relief and clapped.

'You are wrong,' she said to Nostradamus, 'that is the King's last encounter of the day.'

Mary, turning excitedly to Francis, saw that her uncle had entered their box. The scarlet-clad Cardinal stood as silently behind her as Nostradamus behind Catherine – keeping the gamey smell of the arena from his nose with a pomander of ambergris and musk. The King came trotting back from the lists to the box. He was jovial with victory and shouted up to Mary. 'A future queen must have a younger champion. Where's that fool boy? Where's that son of mine?'

Mary, quite unafraid, replied: 'He's not a fool, sir. He's my loving husband.'

Henry laughed, 'I wish he had your spirit, madam, he's a feeble boy. Hey, boy. Show yourself. Find some pleasure in the sport. A future king must be seen to be brave. Come down and ride with me.'

Mary said sharply, 'He is brave, your grace.'

'Don't tell him,' begged Francis from behind her.

'Then send him down,' insisted Henry.

'I will,' said Mary to Francis, furious at the injustice. Then she shouted back at the King, 'He's not afraid for himself but he fears for you. He has twice dreamed that you were dead.'

Henry reacted violently. It was as if this statement of death from his feeble son in some way impugned his courage.

'He's a fool like his mother,' he shouted. 'Superstitious and weak. He's a fool surrounded by fools. We shall see who's going to die.'

He turned and spurred back to the centre of the barrier and raised his hand. The heralds called for silence. When Henry spoke it was in a great shout that echoed all round the arena.

'I shall break a further lance.'

In her box the despised Catherine, who loved him, rose in terror and cried out, 'No, no, my good lord.'

Henry ignored her. 'I choose the captain of the guard of the Queen of Scotland.'

In her box Mary, too, was frightened. Henry shouted, 'Stand forth the Scottish champion.'

The Scottish champion in black armour rode out. The King went to his place at the end of the lists. Catherine left her box and ran to him. Careless of dignity, she held his stirrup and pleaded with him not to break a further lance. This made him more angry. The Scottish champion lowered his helm and couched his lance. The King commanded the Marshall to do his duty and the heralds sounded the fanfare. Catherine was left at the end of the lists in the blazing sunlight when the horses charged. In her box the ape screamed and chattered and jumped so hard against its chain it almost choked on its collar. The two mailed figures clashed at full gallop in the centre and dust rose round them in clouds.

Mary, now sitting in the boat, her hand resting on the head of her young husband, saw again the moment of impact. The lance of the Scottish champion slid off the King's shield and splintered against his golden helm.

9

One huge steel splinter entered through a slit in the helm and almost, it seemed, in slow motion, the King of France rolled from his saddle into the dust clutching at the splinter which had driven through his eye and out of his ear. Inside the helm he was screaming. The small crown of France which topped his helm broke from it and rolled into the dust and blood spilled out from the helm onto it. Catherine de Medici was crying out and running. Francis, heir to the Kingdom, made inarticulate sounds of terror and clung to Mary, who held him and comforted him like a child, cradling him in her arms.

In the boat Francis lifted his head and smiled at her. He took the oars again and began to row. He had rowed three strokes when suddenly he let them go and gasped, 'Mother of God!'

'What is it?' said Mary. 'What is it, Francis? What is it?'

'My head. It's in my head again. In my ear.'

He dropped from the thwart to the bottom of the boat on his knees, his hands clasped round his head, and Mary looked desperately from bank to bank to see if there was anyone to help, but they were alone. She had to climb round him to get to the oars and the boat almost capsized. She sat and began to row towards the bank as he crouched at her feet whimpering. All she could see as she struggled to make headway was that moment, when from the arena in the last of the late afternoon sun, the cortège rode out. Henry had been laid on a cart drawn by two horses and was followed by the armoured knights with standards and lances reversed, pennants dragging in the dust. The people stood in silence, lining the way. Mary had turned and looked over her shoulder at the dead King. Then she had looked at Francis beside her and realized they were now King and Queen of France.

In the royal bedroom, Catherine de Medici sat quite still

and listened to the approaching tumult of the courtiers. The double doors burst open. Two self-important gentlemen of the chamber carried Francis to lay him carefully on the bed. The three doctors who followed were on him like vultures to strip and bleed him, and with them a press of courtiers each with some function that made his gawping presence essential. Mary, struggling through them, tried to get close to Francis to comfort him. She knew how much he dreaded the attentions of the doctors.

Her arm was seized and she was pulled violently round to face her mother-in-law. Catherine spoke softly, but with such venom that Mary recoiled from her greasy and contorted face. 'Are you mad?' said Catherine, 'or do you wish my son dead like his father?'

Mary, almost unable to reply, stammered, 'No, no, madam. You know I love him.'

Catherine said, 'I know that what you've done is stupid and reckless.'

At that moment Francis cried out and Mary turned and shouted, 'Don't hurt him. I forbid you to hurt him.'

She would have beaten her way through to him, but from the doorway behind a voice said sharply, 'Your Majesty.'

She turned and there was the Cardinal and his brother, the Duke of Guise. Obedience to them was strong in her.

'Uncle?' she said.

The Cardinal moved swiftly to her, ignoring Catherine. 'Be patient, my child, you may trust the doctors. We must leave the King to them. Come with me.'

He inclined his head to Catherine, took Mary by the arm and guided her to an alcove on the far side of the room; then he began to speak very softly and quickly.

'It is the third attack this month. He may even die of this illness.'

Even as he spoke, Mary suddenly thought, he has a cruel face. I've always loved and obeyed him. He's my uncle. My mother's brother. And yet he has a cruel face. Cruel and cunning. I wonder why I never thought that before. She replied firmly, 'No, no, he will not,' and tried again to go to the bed where Francis lay moaning. Although she couldn't see what was happening she knew they were bleeding him. The Cardinal gripped her arm to prevent her going.

'We would be very stupid, Mary, not to consider it and the effect upon us if he does.'

Mary said, 'He will not die.'

The Cardinal's tone became sharper. 'You have been married a year. I do not believe you are barren and yet you are not pregnant. Is he impotent? Is that it? Or are you still a virgin? Did he consummate the marriage as you assured me he had? Or did you lie to me?'

Unhesitatingly Mary looked him in the eye and said, 'I will not talk of it, even to you, uncle.'

In contrast to his ascetic brother, the Duke was a large man, and brutally direct.

'You had better, my girl,' he said. 'We're all finished if he dies and there's no child of your body to inherit.'

She suddenly hated his big red face. 'I will not think of life without him,' she was near to tears.

'You must,' said the Cardinal. 'It is quite simple and you must face it. You are the Queen of Scotland and the Isles by birth. No one can take that from you. But you are only the Queen of France by marriage. You are also by right the Queen of England.'

Mary said angrily, 'Mary Tudor rules in England as she should.'

Her gentle heart had been touched when she heard of the sufferings of that Catholic daughter of Henry VIII, whom the English called Bloody Mary, whose womb had swollen with a growth which the poor Queen had taken to be a child.

The Duke said roughly, 'She is dead.'

For a moment Mary forgot Francis.

'Mary Tudor is dead?'

She crossed herself.

'Yes,' said the Duke. 'Mary is dead and they have crowned Elizabeth.'

Mary was stunned by this.

'But after Mary I am the rightful heir to the English throne.'

'Elizabeth reigns.'

'She is illegitimate.'

The Cardinal took her by the arm and turned her and pointed towards the bed.

'Look,' he said, 'if he dies leaving you without an heir, you will lose France because his younger brother will succeed here. The English will not have you if, like Elizabeth, you are childless. So you have to bring him to it. You must act.'

In the background Francis whimpered and cried out again.

'His time is short,' said the Cardinal.

'I won't let him die,' exclaimed Mary, 'do you hear me. I will not let him die.'

Catherine de Medici stood close to her son's pillow as he lay back. Tangled in his damp hair there remained a single flower. She leaned over him and carefully removed it. Then slowly she began to shred it between her fingers. She did not look up as Mary came to the other side of the bed.

In England it was the autumn of the Queen's happiness. On the long September afternoons, when the sun shone day after day from a clear sky, she took her lover on the river to be rowed over the green waters of the Thames to places where no onlooker from the bank could gaze into the open sides of the canopied cabin. Before the cabin the four rowers in royal livery sat in pairs pulling a single oar apiece. Aft of it the discreet coxswain steered the boat. Neither he nor the rowers could see through the thick tapestries into the cabin. They heard laughter, a man's voice singing, the sound of a lute, and sometimes they saw one of the beautiful white hands of the Queen trailing in the water.

In the reign of her half-sister Mary Tudor, the Protestant Elizabeth had been many times near to execution. In the worst moment they had shut her in the Tower of London. A wall's width away Sir Robert Dudley, the son and grandson of beheaded traitors, waited for his own death. This situation, so desperate, so romantic, was heightened by the strange fact that they were both born on the same day and at the same hour. It was in their stars that they should meet. At that time Elizabeth was so poor she could not even pay her few servants. The magnificent Dudley sold land in secret and gave her the money.

In those hard days Elizabeth had had one other friend – Sir William Cecil, first secretary of the kingdom, who had survived in office through four reigns including that of Elizabeth and was not yet forty-five years old.

It was late on a Sunday afternoon when Sir William stood near the landing stage to which the royal barge was returning. As it came alongside Dudley jumped gracefully ashore and helped the Queen. They were laughing at some private joke and at first failed to see the black-clad Cecil in the shade of the trees. When they did they both stopped and Dudley bowed, very formally. Cecil was already bowing to Elizabeth.

'Your grace,' he said, 'my lord.'

His tone was dry. Elizabeth did not reply. She looked hard at him. She knew him better than anyone. It must be very important news to bring him in person. On that glorious day when he had brought her the Coronation ring from the dead Mary's hand she had said to him, 'I have this judgement of you, Sir William Cecil, that you will serve me faithfully. That you will submit neither to bribe nor threat and, despite any judgement that I may make, you will not fail to speak to the contrary if it is for the good of England.'

He had replied, 'Madam, you are the true heir by blood

14

and by Act of Parliament and by confirmation of your sister, Mary Tudor.'

She has the old lion's eyes, thought Cecil, waiting for her to speak, she's half Harry the Eighth – and the other half? Was she a witch, I wonder, Boleyn? Was she a whore? My God, she turned this land upside down. And we're all good Protestants as a result. Elizabeth was still silent. I'm like the Greek messenger of old, he thought wryly. She will want to kill me for the news I bring.

Suddenly Elizabeth smiled and said, 'You have a long face, Master Cecil.'

Without looking at Dudley, Cecil said, 'Madam, this gentleman's wife has just been found dead.'

At what hour, he wondered, had it happened to the healthy and apparently complaisant Amy? Had she fallen downstairs and broken her neck? Or did somebody break it for her? Anyway, it's an ill wind . . . and he, Sir William, was very glad of the corpse at the foot of the stairs.

Dudley was gasping, 'Dead? Amy dead?'

'Of a broken neck at the foot of a staircase in your home.'

He knew that Dudley had not been home for three weeks. While he danced attendance on the Queen at court Amy was required to stay discreetly in the country. Cecil had learned from the almost incoherent servant who brought him the news, that Amy had sent all the servants from the house so that she might be alone that day. Why, he wondered? Why alone? It wasn't suicide. No one could commit suicide in that fashion.

Elizabeth turned her back on them and he thought, is she glad or sorry? In Elizabeth's heart the exultation at the news was so great that she feared to betray herself by showing her face to them. He's free, she thought, he's free. She said without turning, 'When did this terrible accident happen?'

'Many hours ago.'

Elizabeth said, 'I grieve for you, my lord.'

Dudley, with that instinct for self-preservation that had brought him safely out of the Tower, looked hard at Cecil.

'Madam, I do not believe Sir William has told us everything and I would hear it all in your presence.'

Elizabeth said sharply, 'Is there more?'

In his neutral lawyer's voice Cecil said, 'Lady Dudley was alone in the house.'

'So?'

'No servant or retainer, no witness to say how she died.'

'Ah,' said Dudley, 'now we have it. Now I see what Sir William would have you and the whole world think.'

Cecil looked directly at him and said, 'At court there is already talk of murder.'

He thought, now she will rage. If she loves this upstart more than she loves England, then this may finish us both.

Elizabeth did not hesitate. 'Leave me, Sir Robert. Leave the court and stay from it until the matter is investigated.'

Dudley took her hand, kissed it and then turned to go. Cecil smiled with pride at her decision. It was uncharacteristic of him, and Dudley, catching it out of the corner of his eye and believing himself mocked, turned angrily.

'I swear before God and may my soul be blasted in Hell for eternity if I lie, I swear before God, madam, that I have no knowledge of the manner of the death of my wife.'

Then he ran to where his horse was waiting with a groom at its head, jumped into the saddle, dug his heels in and went off at full gallop.

Elizabeth looked at Cecil with hatred. It was a mockery, now, that the sun shone, that the river was green and glittering, that birds flew in the air and all around was that sweet smell of autumn which makes lovers cling to each other. She twisted Dudley's lute between her beautiful hands.

'Now will the great scandal begin,' she said bitterly. 'Now will all my enemies rejoice. Has there been time for your spies at court to find out what the Spanish ambassador makes of this delightful news?'

'He remained silent.'

'And the French ambassador?'

'He exults.'

'What does he say?'

Cecil hesitated and then plunged. 'He says that soon he will see Mary Stuart upon the English throne, for not even the Protestant English will support the bastard and usurper, Elizabeth, when she marries her horsemaster, Dudley, who has killed his wife to make room for her.'

When the lute smashed against the tree the bridge broke and the strings whipped back against her hand. She said, 'I will give him another.' And then she shouted at Cecil, 'He is innocent – innocent.'

'Then let him prove it.'

'When I was in great danger in the reign of my late sister he did not desert me *and I will not desert him*.'

'You are in great danger *now* from Mary Stuart and the Catholic cause.'

'Mary Stuart is safe in France for a lifetime.'

Safe, thought Cecil, with a sickly young husband, scheming uncles? He said, 'Please remember, your grace, that her mother rules as regent in Scotland.'

Now Elizabeth had an object for the rage that seemed to choke her. 'Mary Stuart's mother does not *rule* in Scotland,' she exploded. 'She tyrannizes Scotland with a French army. She forces the Catholic faith down Scottish throats. Half her nobles are Protestant and in open rebellion against her. Rule, you say? She barely survives. I fear neither Mary Stuart in France nor her mother in Scotland.'

She threw the broken lute into the river and walked away from Cecil, along the bank to the narrow country road where her coach waited. Cecil hurried to follow her. Guilty or innocent, he thought, she will save him if she can and he braced himself to convince her of her only duty.

'Then I must ask you, do you not fear your own Catholic nobles who live in the North hard upon the Scottish border?'

For a moment Elizabeth was staggered and forgot her anger. 'Why should I? They are not persecuted. I am no tyrant. They worship as they please. They are free men.'

'Madam,' said Cecil in deadly earnest, 'Scotland is the back door to England. It must not be unbarred by a scandal in the English court. If you protect Sir Robert Dudley and seem to condone a murder, your Northern lords will believe that next you will marry him. The rumour is everywhere. Rather than have him as their king they will certainly rebel against you.'

Elizabeth suddenly stopped and sat down on the edge of the path with her back against a tree. Cecil had won and she felt ill, as she often did in times of crisis.

'Very well,' she said after a moment, 'bring him to trial in open court and hide nothing.'

He bowed. She closed her eyes.

'And, Cecil — '

'Your grace?'

'Send gold at once to the Scottish rebels. Not only gold but an army, for I will see their cause triumph in Scotland. And, Cecil —'

'Your grace?'

'See that they do not line their own pockets with my money.'

He thought, as he waited to help her to her feet when she felt well enough, there are wonderful days when all my prayers are answered. God be praised.

Mary of Guise, mother of Mary, Queen of Scots, was old, swollen with dropsy and solitary in an alien land. For sixteen years, since her husband James V died of wounds, she had bravely held the throne for her daughter. Now she faced siege. The English army and English gold sent by

Elizabeth put heart into the Protestant rebels. She sat high on the walls of Edinburgh Castle and looked out at them camped in front of the city. She confided her thoughts to no one. But when she prayed it was that she would live long enough to win the battle and give the Kingdom back to her daughter. The artillery began and day and night the English batteries flashed and roared. After a week the town was on fire. Fanned by fresh breezes from the sea, flames rose into the sky and lit the masts and spars of the English fleet.

Certain of victory the whole English line advanced and with them a thousand Scots. But they came to a wide moat and beyond it a huge stone wall; and it was there that they found their scaling ladders were too short by six feet. They were trapped in their thousands below the walls. Those in front tried to push back. Those behind tried to push on, and the defenders on the walls exultantly poured down shot from cannon, hurled huge blocks of stone and sent down blazing pitch in barrels. The French harlots, as they were called, those Scottish women who loved their Frenchmen and fought beside them, joined the men on the battlements and helped to load the cannon and roll the barrels of tar. For two hours the invaders attempted to scale the walls.

When half their officers were dead and eight hundred of the soldiers were either dead or wounded the bugles sounded the retreat. Mary of Guise went to Mass and praised God for the victory. The French soldiers stripped the dead naked and laid their carcasses in rows under the hot sun.

The messenger who brought the news to Cecil had ridden for four days. Cecil read the dispatch twice and then sought private audience with the Queen. She was reading when he entered her privy chamber and she did not look up. She said, 'My Greek has grown rusty of late, Master Cecil. I must improve it for I am more afraid of making a fault in that than of the Kings of France and Spain, of Mary, Queen of Scots, the Guise family and all their confederates.'

She knows, thought Cecil, she has been told. He said formally, 'We have suffered a disastrous defeat in Scotland.'

She did not reply. He said, 'But there is one hope. Mary of Guise is dying. Of this I am certain. When she dies the Protestants will triumph. It is she alone who inspires the Catholic cause.'

Elizabeth said sharply, 'Do you rejoice at the prospect of the death of a queen?'

'She is a Papist and an enemy of England.'

'Papist or not, enemy or not, she is a queen.'

'But your grace, it is you who wish her destroyed.'

'Cast down, but not dead,' said Elizabeth at once. 'Her army destroyed, but her life spared. I do not relish the thought of the death of any queen. It is too close to our person. We are defeated you say?'

'Yes.'

Elizabeth banged down her book in anger and stood up. 'Well you are wrong. We are not defeated and we shall not cry over spilt milk. I am sorry that the success was no better, but considering the importance of the matter I shall neither suffer delay nor retire from the field. Send more men and money and supplies with all possible speed.'

'How many men?' asked Cecil cautiously.

'Four thousand,' she replied at once. 'And see that they lack nothing to accomplish the enterprise. More than that, see that our ships bar the way to any reinforcements from France. We shall starve her out – this dying queen – if we must.'

She has said nothing of Dudley since she banished him from court, thought Cecil, and she acts with vigour and decision. Perhaps after all it was only infatuation. Thank God for the death of the good Amy if it has removed that danger from court and cleared the way for her to marry a prince.

CHAPTER TWO

In the stables they brought the King's horse from its stall. The animal, scenting the fear on them, reared and plunged, injuring a groom. Finally they had it saddled and bridled and began to lead it through into the courtyard. Before they reached it they could hear other servants shouting again for the King's horse as they ran from the château with torches to light the way for Francis. Mary came close after him pleading with him to go back inside. Following her were Mary Fleming and Mary Seton.

Francis cried out as they brought the horse to him, 'I will ride from the pain. It goes when I ride.'

The grooms helped him to the saddle and he pulled hard on the jaw-breaker bit, forcing the horse in a cruel circle, and then was away at a gallop. Mary was left, lit by a ring of torches. Seton put a cloak round her shoulders and said, 'Please come back inside, your grace.'

'No.'

'Twice this month his Majesty has ridden his horse to death. He may be away for many hours.'

'I must keep vigil for him. Bring a chair. The rest of you may go. Go now. Leave me.'

They brought a chair and she sat. They left her alone. She wrapped the cloak tight round her. She was half-stupefied by fatigue. She could think of nothing to do except pray. She clasped her hands together like a child, turned her face up towards the night sky and said out loud, 'Almighty God, if you love the King more than I, then take him to you. But take me as well for I have no wish to live without him.'

The response from the dark shadows on the far side of the courtyard was a vulgar shout of laughter.

'Who's that?' she cried. 'Who's that?'

A man on horseback rode briskly out of the shadows, dismounted and strode towards her with such vigour that she rose as if to ward him off. He stopped before her, took off his hat with a flourish, bowed and said, 'James Hepburn, Lord Bothwell.'

He had the look of an eagle and he stank of sweat and the saddle. Mary, used to the most elaborate and richly dressed court in Europe, was astonished by the rough, wild look of him.

He said, 'I am an emissary from your brother, the Lord James Stuart, regent of Scotland.'

'My mother is the regent in Scotland, not James.'

'I am sent to tell you that your mother is dead.'

She shook her head, unable to speak.

He repeated, 'Your mother is dead.'

'No.'

'I am sent here by your brother to prepare you.'

Will she faint, he thought, she's a feeble enough girl and possibly soft in the head to sit out here on a cold night praying. It's a poor lookout for the Stuart line.

She was looking past him, hoping desperately for the return of Francis. She was numb with shock.

'Madam,' he said impatiently, 'your mother is dead. The French are defeated as a result and the remnant of them are coming home.'

By God, he thought, it strains a man's loyalty to have ridden this far for such a reception.

Mary walked past him to his horse and began to stroke its muzzle. It seemed to comfort her.

'This is my home,' she said distractedly. 'France is my home.'

'You are needed in Scotland.'

'No,' she said. 'I am needed here.'

My mother is dead, she thought, as she ran her fingers gently over the velvet muzzle of the horse. She is dead. I did not know how much I loved her even though I saw little of her. But surely nothing will happen to Francis? Not now. If God has taken my mother He will leave me my husband.

'This is a fine animal,' she said. 'Forgive me, but I have had little sleep recently and my mind is not clear. Tell me again who you are.'

'I am,' said Bothwell, 'the Lord Bothwell, Lieutenant of the Border.'

'And of what faith are you?' said Mary.

He laughed out loud. 'God, your grace, whether Catholic or Protestant, is a bogey to frighten little children in the nursery.'

She said mechanically, 'That is blasphemy.'

'So you say, but you will find me a loyal man.'

'I find you insolent.'

Ah, he thought, she has some spirit. Excellent.

'Forgive me,' he said. 'I did not intend it.'

'Stable your horse,' she said. 'It is shivering.'

They found the king at dawn. The trees were dark over him. Birds sang although it was late in the year. His horse cropped grass under the trees, its reins trailing, one of them still clasped in his dead hand. The peasants brought him to the château on a cart, like his father before him, with the horse tied to the back.

In the courtyard the two widows waited. As the cart trundled into the yard, the ape suddenly broke free from the grip of the dwarf and ran to it. The awed peasants dropped the shaft as the ape jumped up beside the body of the King and chattered over it.

He lay in state for the decadent and scented courtiers to pay their last homage. Then his heart was removed and enclosed in a leaden vase. On the night before that happened, as Mary knelt in vigil beside him, Catherine and her uncles came wrangling and quarrelling to find her. She was a marriage prize. The fortunes of the Guise family rested in her.

Catherine said as she entered, 'She shall leave my court when the period of mourning is over – arrange your marriages elsewhere.'

'Six months,' said the Cardinal. 'A bare six months only, to marry her to a Catholic prince in all ceremony here in the court of France and then she will leave, I promise you.'

The Duke said, 'For Scotland with an army. She will take back what is hers. But she must have a powerful husband to support her.'

Two other men had been waiting patiently for Mary. They overheard this conversation and one of them stepped forward. It was Bothwell.

'That will be the end of the Stuarts in Scotland, I promise you. My people will never again submit to a foreign army.'

Catherine looked down at her son.

'Against my will,' she said, 'he married her. Now he is dead and she is the cause.'

Mary rose from her knees.

'No,' she said. 'No. I loved him. I nursed him. I am not the cause.'

Catherine ignored her and went on, 'I rule here until my second son is of age. If you defy me, my lords, I will not only banish her from the court, I will exile her from France.'

She turned and left. Mary looked towards the other man.

'Brother,' she said, 'help me.'

From the shadows the Lord James Stuart stepped forward and took her outstretched hands in his. He was shorter than she. Dark, heavy-shouldered and brutal of face. A dour fighting man it seemed. But when he spoke his voice was gentle and in contrast to his appearance.

'What shall I do?' said Mary. 'You were always kind to

me when we were children together. Help me now, James.'

'Mary,' he said, 'if you wish it I will take you home to Scotland. There you shall reign. You are the rightful Queen. You have no need of foreign marriages or foreign armies.'

The Duke said, 'Ask him the price.'

'There is no price. There is a simple fact. In Scotland you, a devout Catholic Queen, must tolerate the Protestant religion of your subjects because it has taken the deepest roots there.'

Mary said, 'I have been away so long. Will they remember me? Will I be happy? Will the people love me?'

Now is the moment to put some heart into her, thought Bothwell, and he said cheerfully, 'Tolerate the new religion, your grace, and they will give you their hearts.'

'She shall not,' said the Cardinal.

Mary looked at the tall, scarlet figure with the dark Duke beside him and she knew that without her, their power would crumble. She felt no pity for them, for they in their turn had not pitied Francis when he was ill. And their sorrow over the death of their sister, Mary of Guise, was merely sorrow for a battle lost. She could respect them still but she could not love them. Then she looked at her half-brother and Bothwell. I am of neither world, she thought, and I am only eighteen. I cannot live out my life in exile.

She said, 'Uncle, I must do it.'

Another thought came to her. 'Elizabeth will be my neighbour.'

'Yes,' replied the Cardinal grimly. 'And she has half your nobles in her pocket.'

'I know,' she replied unexpectedly, 'but now everything is changed both for Scotland and for me. My mother is dead and the French army has come home.' She looked sadly down, 'And he is dead so I must make a new beginning with Elizabeth as well as with my own Protestant subjects.'

As she said this she saw the way to begin. 'I will travel to Scotland through England. I will go to the court of

Elizabeth and meet her face to face, win her friendship and, in this way, begin to put all sorrow behind me and start a new life.'

James Stuart kissed her hand.

'Your grace,' he said, 'my dear sister. I will return at once to Scotland to prepare everything for your arrival.'

Even Bothwell was impressed.

'Your grace,' he said, 'I will see to everything here, and then bring you safely home to your kingdom.'

'I thank you both with all my heart,' said Mary.

They left her. The pain in her knees and back from kneeling became so great that she could not pray.

At some time in the night she dozed. She dreamed of her marriage day. Over her head the roof of the huge pavilion was of Cyprus silk, spangled with golden fleurs-de-lis. On the ground was a vast blue carpet stamped with golden lilies. The glittering nobility of France awaited them. They were mounted, and surrounded by musicians dressed in red and yellow. Servants pulled the two full-sized dummy horses into the light of a thousand candles. Francis sat on a golden horse and Mary's was of silver. She was delirious with happiness but Francis, worried by the sound and his exposed position, was nervous. She put her hand out to take his. As she did so it seemed that a shadow lay between them. The gaunt figure of Nostradamus moved from beside Catherine de Medici and made a strange sign in the air, and in her dream Mary cried out. Then Catherine was on her knees at an altar before Nostradamus celebrating the Mass; the baby's throat gaped; blood ran into the chalice. Mary was falling from the horse. She woke to find herself lying against the bier. The candles were low. It was bitter in the pre-dawn. Something stirred in the shadows and she gasped.

'Don't be afraid.'

Bothwell's voice.

'Why are you here?'

'It is my duty to guard the Queen of Scotland while she is in my care.'

'Leave me,' she said.

'Come,' said Bothwell firmly, 'leave him. He'll do well enough without you. What you need is breakfast and the light of day.'

To her surprise she found herself taking Bothwell's hand. One leg was dead and she was forced to lean on him. She looked at Francis for the last time.

As he took her towards the door Bothwell said firmly, 'You have your life in front of you.'

He glanced over his shoulder at the bier.

'We never know when death will come, so let us make the most of the days.'

'Where's my brother?'

'On his way to Scotland,' said Bothwell. 'Now there is a man who wastes no time in idle thought.'

Something in his tone of voice surprised her and she said, 'Don't you like him?'

He smiled. 'Madam,' he said, 'if you are to survive you must learn something which in all the seventeen years your mother held the throne for you she never understood. The ferocity of the hatred of the clans for each other is so great that rather than see a single one of them raised above the rest they will put the Devil himself upon the throne of Scotland; so we must have the Stuarts. But not, madam, your half-brother. You, the rightful Queen.'

'That is not a flattering reason,' she said.

They were in the long echoing corridor outside. He stopped, looked hard at her and said, 'You'll get very little flattery in Scotland and when you do, distrust it.'

The trumpets sounded to announce the supper. Elizabeth, dressed in purple velvet, with gold and many pearls and jewels adding greatly to her beauty, led her guests into the long gallery at Whitehall. It was draped with gold and

27

silver brocade and the air was full of the scent of the flowers which filled it. The farthingales of the women were so large there was not room for them all at the tables. Some of them had to sit on the rush-covered floor to be served their supper.

At the Queen's own small table her French guests drank from cups of gold and of rock crystal. She smiled at them; flirted with them; danced with them; told them of her joy in the love of her people, but gave them no answer concerning a passport for Mary Stuart. Late in the evening she sent them on their way with rich gifts. Then she hurried into the Palace to the council chamber.

The two men waiting for her bowed.

'I will not,' she said at once, 'have any dealings with that lady, and I will stop her by force if I must from returning to Scotland. She claims my throne, and she has the arms of England quartered upon the arms of France.'

Cecil, tired from the endless administration of the State which filled his days from dawn to late each night, said wearily, 'That is unwise.'

His foot hurt him. It was the first twinge of gout, later to cripple him.

'Sit down, sit down,' she ordered. 'I'm tired of your long face. Would you have me meet her? Shall I compromise my position? I will have nothing of her.'

'Not meet her,' replied Cecil patiently, 'but do nothing to impede her return to Scotland.'

'Why?'

The other man spoke: it was James Stuart. During the rebellion against Mary's mother he had personally come to the English court to meet Elizabeth and collect gold to pay his soldiers. He admired her. He said with complete conviction, 'Because, your Majesty, if we do not bring her back to Scotland subservient to a Protestant court, she will soon arrive back with a Catholic army at her back. Her uncles will see to that.'

28

'And then,' said Cecil, 'you will hear her knocking on the back door.'

'And what will stop her doing that now?' replied Elizabeth. 'Are the Protestant Lords of the Congregation in Scotland so devoted to me?'

'Madam, I am first among them,' replied Stuart, 'and I am devoted to peace and order in our two lands. Once we have her safe in Edinburgh there is no further danger. Mary Stuart will rule in name. I will rule in fact.'

You may well, thought Elizabeth. Reason is on your side, but if that lady has the true instincts of a queen you will not survive for ever. If it were me I would find a way to pull you down. But I want no more wars. No more money wasted.

She said, 'If you value my friendship you will keep that promise.'

'Then shall she come home?' asked Cecil.

'Yes,' replied Elizabeth. 'But not through my realm.'

She left them and went to her chamber and could not sleep for thinking of Dudley. After midnight she woke her ladies and bullied and shouted at them, reducing them to tears, and felt no better for it. Towards dawn she slept. She dreamed, and in her dream her father, Henry VIII whom she loved and hated, stood with a long sword in his hand from which the blood was dripping. From the ground her mother's head looked up at her and said, 'You are safe while you dance. You are safe while you dance, Elizabeth.'

She woke sweating and it was too late in the year for birds to be singing in the grey morning light.

In the council chamber, when the door closed behind her, Stuart said, 'If I am to keep that promise there is something we must do.'

And he began to describe in detail to Cecil the action that English ships must take off the coast of Northumberland.

CHAPTER THREE

Gulls wheeled, screaming in the heavy sky over the two great galleons at Calais. As the capstans turned and the anchors broke ground the sound of bosuns' pipes almost equalled the sound of the gulls. The sharp wind from the south-west bellied the sails as they were hoisted and set and the two galleons lay over and began their run out into the Channel at the beginning of the six-hundred-mile journey to Scotland. At the mainmast head of the first galleon, flagship of the French fleet, flew the Scottish colours. Mary stood in the stern by the steersman holding the taffrail and looking back at the coast of France.

There, on the quay at Calais, were gathered the nobility, the poets, the singers and the men of the Church who had come to bid her farewell. She could still discern the scarlet figure of her uncle.

It was like a dream or a fever. Am I really in this ship? Can I really smell the sea, hear the gulls? Is the deck slanted under my feet? Are those my uneasy ladies huddled there? Shall I ever see that land again? Out loud she said, 'Farewell France.' But she could not believe the words as she uttered them.

By the opposite rail, deep in conversation, were the two men whom her uncle, the Cardinal, had brought to her that morning. A tall, heavy priest, and an Italian.

The conversation when she met them first, five hours earlier, ran in her head. She had been standing, amazed, with Elizabeth's letter in her hand. She was shocked by it.

'She refuses, me safe conduct through England.' And then, as she read on, 'She hates me.'

The Duke said, 'She fears you.'

'She says I must renounce my claim to the English throne.'

She tore the document to pieces.

'I renounce nothing, neither my voyage home to Scotland nor my true claim to the English throne.'

A voice behind her said, 'For that is the ruling of Holy Mother Church. You are the English Queen. Elizabeth is bastard and heretic.'

She turned. The Cardinal had joined them, and with him the priest and another man. The priest repeated, 'You are the English Queen.'

His accent was English and she was astounded.

'Who is this priest, uncle?'

The Cardinal replied, 'Father Ballard, your new chaplain and confessor.'

'An English priest? My confessor?'

She made no attempt to hide her surprise and displeasure. Ballard, who feared nothing on earth, said at once, 'There are no longer Englishmen or Frenchmen or Scotsmen. There are, in all life and death matters, only two sorts of man – Catholic and heretic – only a fool thinks otherwise.'

'Guard your tongue,' said the Duke, 'and get to the ship.'

'No,' said Mary. She was impressed. 'He is right and I shall not forget it.'

The Cardinal said, 'May I present David Riccio, a singer from Italy.'

The other man, small and monkey-like, came forward grinning all over his face. There was an engaging comic quality about him and his Italian accent. He said, 'I have travelled far to serve you, your grace.'

She replied, smiling, 'Well we still have far to go.'

She took her uncles to one side. 'Only two sorts of men? Which sort are the English priest and the little Italian?'

'The priest is a Jesuit,' said the Cardinal, 'serving the true Queen of England, yourself. You may trust him with your life.'

'And the singer,' said the Duke, 'is the Pope's agent.'

She did not immediately understand. The Duke said, 'Yours will be a Protestant court. You need a safe and secret way to your real friends. Riccio is the way. Let him seem to sing for his supper. Promote him slowly, but trust him. He speaks many languages and is expert with cyphers.'

She laughed out loud and for the first time in many months her normal high spirits were revived.

'Cyphers,' she said, 'I shall enjoy the secret work.'

As she watched them by the rail of the ship they turned from it and began solemnly to walk the deck, the small Riccio taking two paces to every stride of his companion. The sea wind nipped her face and Mary Fleming, looking at her, thought, how beautiful she is. How young and how beautiful.

Mary turned to look over the stern of the ship towards the second galleon which was keeping station with them. Bothwell was on the rail forward steadying himself by a rope stay. In the hold of that ship were her six white horses. Bothwell chose to sail with them to supervise their stowage so that they would not be hurt or break a leg on the voyage.

He had said, 'We shall next meet in the port of Leith, your grace, where I shall land your horses fit for your triumphal ride.'

Impulsively she had replied, 'Bothwell, shall I ride in triumph? Will all be well?'

'There's only one question, your grace, will you rule the Scottish lords or will they rule you?'

With certainty, 'I shall rule the Scottish lords.'

'I wish you then,' he said, 'Queen Mary Stuart, *bon voyage*.'

The wind was rising and the galleons began to pitch and roll. The galley slaves between decks, chained to their benches, were glad of it. The more wind the less work. When she stepped aboard the ship Mary had said to the captain, 'No slave must be beaten during this voyage.'

They were glad of that too, for the word came down to them swiftly in the mysterious way that news always passes among imprisoned men.

In England, Elizabeth graciously changed her mind concerning a passport for Mary and personally handed the document to the French ambassador. She appeared genuinely distressed when she was told that it was too late, for Mary was already three days at sea.

It was low tide. Mud spattered the flimsy shoes, the stockings and the lifted hems as the women picked their way from the beached boat to the firmer ground above. As the mist cleared in front of them, they saw overturned cannon, broken weapons rusting, a ripped banner and the bones of bodies that had lain out in the sun until pecked white by the birds.

Mary said, 'Where are we in the name of God? What is this foul place? Why is there no one here to greet me?'

Riccio, close behind her said, 'Speak softly, madam. They are not far away. I hear them.'

They stopped. From behind the high shingle ridge that topped the foreshore came the sound of horses and bridles and the voices of men. Suddenly there appeared on the ridge the Lords of the Congregation of Scotland, all mounted, and led by James Stuart.

Mary and her party stared at them in amazement and even Ballard, who was quite fearless and looked forward to the new life which death would bring him, was awed. There could have been no greater contrast between these lords and the lords in the court of France. Their beards were thick, not trimmed and scented. Their clothes were of coarse materials. They wore belts with great buckles and carried heavy fighting weapons, claymores not rapiers. Immediately behind James rode the tall and consumptive Ruthven, next to him

33

the brutal Morton and near him the wild Huntly. Riccio counted fifteen others. The French guards who accompanied Mary's pitifully small court moved as if they would defend her as Stuart rode down to her.

When he dismounted before her he made no attempt to bow and said harshly, 'Good health to your Majesty and welcome to Scotland.'

Believing him still the friend from her childhood and the loving brother who had helped her to make the decision in France, she said, 'What has happened, James? Where are my people?'

'For five days,' he replied, 'the fog has lain over the land and you were not expected so soon, that is all.'

She was puzzled.

'But you are here?'

'We rode hard when the warning gun fired. Your loyal Lords of the Congregation welcome you.'

So that's it, she thought, they are taken by surprise, that is all, and she was relieved.

'I understand,' she said. 'Then soon the royal guards will arrive from Edinburgh, and the carpet for me to walk upon and a canopy over my head.'

'No, madam,' he said. 'There will be nothing.' He raised his voice so that the other lords could hear him. 'We can waste no money on idle show.'

The lords, all of them still mounted and looking down on Mary's party, growled with approval. Stuart's words and the ugly sound from the lords shocked Mary's followers. Her four ladies, in particular, were outraged and moved closer to her as if to support her. Stuart, seeing this, deliberately went on, 'This is not France.'

Her only thought was to go. She turned her back on him and she would have walked back to the boat had not Riccio stepped firmly in her way and shouted in a very loud and cheerful voice, 'God bless Scotland.'

Mary came to her senses. Riccio bowed before her very

elaborately to make a clown of himself and draw attention away from the Queen.

'And God bless the Scottish Queen who is so near her throne at last.'

Yes I am, she thought, yes I am. She forced herself to turn and face her half-brother. Deliberately she smiled her most charming and melting smile. She raised her voice so that all should hear and she said, 'My Lords of the Congregation you do me great honour to ride in such haste to meet me. My good brother is wise to waste no money upon ceremony.'

She looked directly at him, hiding misery and disgust.

'Brother, I embrace you for your wisdom and before these lords I name you my chief minister.'

She forced herself to go to him and kiss him on both cheeks in the French fashion. Riccio at once began to applaud and, catching his eye, Ballard took it up, then the ladies and all the French servants. The dashing Huntly took off his bonnet and waved it in approval and shouted, 'God save the Queen!'

The grim lords round him did the same and the roar, 'God save the Queen!' echoed along the seashore at Leith. Stuart, momentarily at a disadvantage, could only say, 'I thank you, dear sister.'

Then he shouted, 'Bring the horses. Bring the Queen's horses.'

The Lords of the Congregation broke away, walking their beasts to right and left, and into view over the ridge came grooms leading five or six poor animals with their ribs sticking out. At first Mary could not believe these horses were intended for her and her party and when she saw they were she said quietly to Stuart, 'These are not mine. I will wait until my horses have landed.'

Stuart replied, 'Your stable was taken by the English.'

Mary thought at first that this was some further attempt to humiliate her.

'Taken?' she said, 'How could that be? They are in the other ship. Bothwell has them safe.'

'That ship was captured. It had no safe conduct through English waters Elizabeth's ambassador has already complained to me.'

Then she realized it was true.

'And Bothwell? What has happened to him? Is he captured or dead?'

'They have him safely,' said Stuart.

'And I will have him back,' flared Mary. 'Ransom him. Arrange it at once.'

'He is not for ransom.'

Somewhere in the back of her mind a thought had been forming since the moment he mentioned the English ambassador. She said, 'It is only three days since the two ships parted company in the fog and yet you, brother, know everything of its fate and the fate of Lord Bothwell. Even the fastest horseman could not ride from London to Edinburgh in three days.'

Stuart went to the nearest of the wretched horses and taking it by the bridle led it to her.

'Will you mount, your Majesty,' he said. 'It is a sharp morning and we must move on.'

She realized that they were all looking at her – the Lords of the Congregation, her servants, the French sailors from the ship. All were focused upon her and Stuart to see what she would do. She raised her voice for them to hear. 'Yes,' she said, 'gladly. I have lived for this day when I would return to Scotland and my people.'

James looked admiringly at her.

'Well spoken,' he said ironically.

In the next hour Mary Stuart came near to despair. From her childhood she had lived in a world of elegance and fine architecture; of Gobelin tapestries, hunting leopards, pageantry and peacocks spreading their feathers; of rich food, fine music, sycophantic poets and the glory of High Mass. She had loved the glittering life of the richest court in Europe.

On the short ride from Leith to Holyrood she saw the terrible poverty of the Scots. All round were still the signs of battle; and in the air, it seemed to her, a sense of black and forbidding bigotry.

This feeling was so strong that she felt no shock when a harsh Scots voice cried out from the height above a defile through which they were riding, 'I have prayed that this Queen might die like her mother before her.'

They stopped and Mary looked up at him. He was of middle size, powerful and thick-set, his beard was long and he had the eye of a madman or fanatic.

'Who is he?'

'John Knox, madam, the head of our Church.'

'Your Church, not mine, brother.'

Knox, the ex-Catholic priest, the ex-galley slave, head, fount and driving force of the Reformation in Scotland, pointed down.

'See what she brings with her – a priest. Better that she'd come with French troops again, for she will comfort the Papists we have driven from this land – monks, friars, priests, nuns and all such filthy persons. One Mass is more fearful than ten thousand soldiers.'

'Not to me, sir,' cried out Mary.

'Do you defend the Mass?'

'I defend the Church of Rome,' she said, 'for that I think is the true Church of God.'

'Ride on,' said Stuart.

'No,' replied Mary, and called again to Knox. 'I will bear with patience your ugly words, John Knox, for you, like all my subjects, shall have the free use of your conscience and I the free use of mine.'

Stuart shouted, 'Ride on!'

In her head Mary heard Bothwell ask, 'Will you rule the lords or will they rule you?' No matter what it costs, she thought, I will rule here.

John Knox, looking down as they rode away said out loud, 'Whore. Papist whore.'

Then he mounted his horse and rode back to his house in Edinburgh to prepare a long sermon to be delivered against her from the pulpit of St Giles the following Sunday.

An orange sun was low in a dove-grey winter sky when Elizabeth began her morning walk from the Palace of Windsor. She walked briskly. She was warmly wrapped against the bitter and bracing morning air. The weather in England had changed in recent winters. It was not unusual for rivers to freeze over and, in the poor country districts, for children to get frost-bite. Elizabeth, who loved dancing and riding and all forms of exercise, revelled in the sharpness of it.

She was walking down the centre of a broad ride, lined on either side by English oaks, when she first saw the six white horses in the paddock from a distance of about a quarter of a mile. Momentarily, she checked in her stride and the ladies and gentlemen who attended her some paces behind, also stopped. The sight of the horses caused an extraordinary jolt in her mind. Suddenly Mary Stuart, her Catholic rival of whom she'd heard so much from her ambassadors in France, became a reality. She had owned these horses, chosen them, loved them. Following hard on the first thought came the second. Is she a better horsewoman than I? And with it a sharp pang of jealousy. Mary was not just the symbol of the Catholic challenge, but a flesh and blood rival.

The grooms were up and when they saw the Queen approaching they began to trot the horses. The breath streamed from their snorting nostrils as they tried to take the bits to canter and gallop. The grooms held them with difficulty and Elizabeth thought, how she must miss them.

On the far side of the paddock a horseman was approaching. His back was to the low sun but the shape was unmistakeable. She picked up her skirts and began to run. Her courtiers were startled. In the paddock the grooms took the white horses from a trot to a canter and the sound of their hooves on the turf filled the clear morning air. Elizabeth was panting and running. The horseman put his horse to the gallop. Five yards from her he reined up, jumped from the saddle and ran to her where she now stood waiting for him, knelt to her, took her hands and kissed them both. She looked down at his bent head and almost knelt so that her face would be level with his. She stopped herself and when she spoke her voice was sharp, almost hostile. Her greatest fear was that at some time passion would overcome her judgement. She removed her hands from his and stepped back from him.

'Well, Robin?'

He rose. He was smiling.

'My wife's death is judged to be an accident. I am declared innocent, your Majesty, despite all efforts of Cecil's spies to find evidence against me in the matter.'

'Then you are indeed innocent, so you may return to court.'

'If you permit it.'

'I order it. Come,' she said, 'look what we have taken from the Queen of Scotland. And we have safely in the Tower a Scottish lord who has given us great trouble on the borders in the past – Bothwell.'

I wouldn't be in his shoes, thought Dudley, remembering All Hallows Eve two years before when the messenger carrying gold to encourage the rebellion in Scotland had been waylaid. Three thousand pounds had been brought in a portmanteau from London. The Queen's English messenger had an anxious time as he rode North. He was dogged by spies all the way and at the border he was glad to hand the money over. It was mainly in French crowns, for the crafty Cecil, with his attention to detail, had no desire that it should be traced back to the Treasury of Elizabeth. Nobody cared if the French guessed where the rebels got their money from, but there must be no evidence to hold up in the French court. A certain John Cockburn was entrusted with the last leg of the journey. He got, with the money, a promise of gunpowder and munitions.

John Cockburn was a cocky man. He knew, he said, every last track in his native Scotland on the border so he travelled in the dark night. Towards four in the morning when he was leading his horse, the path being so bad, he heard the sound of leather creaking and a horse's hoof, and he caught in the faint light a flash of steel. It was the last thing he ever saw in this life. Bothwell cut his head from his shoulders with one stroke of his claymore and then with the same bloody sword he cut the portmanteau full of money from the saddle bar and rode off. John Cockburn's two servants brought the story back to the governor of Newcastle.

'So you have him in the Tower, madam?'

'I have,' she said.

'That is a cold place to sleep.'

They smiled at each other, remembering how it was to lie in the Tower waiting for death.

'You will sleep in a warmer one,' said Elizabeth, 'now that you are free to return to court. I order you to take the apartment above my own. I believe, Robin, that I shall have need of your advice constantly.'

Dudley said at once with great passion, 'If you would have me constantly at your side, then marry me, my love.'

Elizabeth turned on him as if he had struck her.

'In this land,' she said, 'there will be but one mistress and no master.'

Dudley instantly responded.

'Then I will come no more to your court. I will leave this land. I will sail for the Indies.'

He turned from her to return to his horse.

'You – shall – not!'

No man in the land would have disobeyed. He stopped. She flayed him.

'You are my master of horse, although some say you are my little dog for when they see you enter a chamber they know I will come soon after. And again when they gibe at me in Catholic courts, they say that the horsemaster freely mounts the Queen and now would put a bridle on her. You are the son and the grandson of traitors. How dare you speak of marriage to me.'

He had never seen her so angry and he knew it was no put-on emotion as she so often did for the benefit of ambassadors and courtiers who displeased her. At that moment he was afraid of her, but it was not in him to see that she spoke so cruelly because, in her deepest heart, she had permitted herself to think of marriage on the day when she had heard of the death of his wife.

'Forgive me,' he said. 'It was my delight in seeing you again. My love for you is so great that I cannot be wise or discreet.'

'Your head itches for a crown.'

She turned and pointed at the horses. On the other side of the paddock her attendants, greedy for gossip, longed to know what was passing between them.

'You are a commoner and commoners do not marry queens. Attend to your common business, horsemaster. Keep the Scottish Queen's horses well. It may suit me to return them one day.'

He bowed formally and turned and mounted his horse. She was struck by a thought.

She said softly, 'The Scottish Queen. Now there is a pretty widow for an ambitious lord whose head itches for a crown.'

And the plan to destroy Mary formed itself completely in that moment. Dudley, aware that she had spoken but not hearing what she said, turned back.

'Your grace?'

'I said, Robin, that you shall dine with me tonight. And then we will keep each other loving company until the morning.'

Her attendants saw she was smiling.

Mary, Queen of Scotland and the Isles, stood in the centre of a bare room in Holyrood Palace and shivered with the cold. The Palace was not ready for her occupation. The lords had assumed that she would go to Edinburgh Castle and this she flatly refused The huge, grey, ominous pile which dominated the city so depressed her that she would not go near it. She associated it with the defeat of her mother and the melancholy aftermath.

The door opened and Stuart entered. Immediately forgetting her intention to be subtle and devious she burst out, 'You have humiliated me.'

He was genuinely surprised and could think only of the intervention of John Knox on their journey towards Edinburgh.

'You shall keep your religion,' he said, 'but be more prudent in future.'

'And,' replied Mary, 'shall I rule here?'

She topped him by two inches He was forced to look up at her. It did not seem to disconcert him as it did many men.

'Sister,' he said, 'we must have no illusions, you and I. We shared a father in James V of Scotland but I came out on the wrong side of the blanket and it is the fate of the bastard sons of kings never to be kings themselves. This I accepted long ago. I have no ambition for your Crown and I will resist any man who tries to take it from you. You are the Queen. As for humiliation, your people will love you better for a humble beginning. Your voice, your clothes, your manners and those you bring with you remind us of the flaunting and hated French Papists of your mother's court. To ride here in triumph on a stable of white horses, spattering mud on the common people, would not endear you to them.'

'I am the Queen,' she said, 'but you will rule.'

As if she had not spoken he went on, 'I want you to be happy. You shall have dancing and hunting and music and good eating. Leave the troubles of State to me.'

To defeat him and rule she must convince him that she was no danger to him. She made her voice sound apologetic when she said, 'Please forgive me for my anger. I am very tired from the journey. I see that you are kind and would spare me the tedium of State matters of which I know nothing. This country is strange to me and I will be happy to do as you wish.'

'Good,' said James Stuart. 'Good. You have made a brave beginning after a hard and dangerous journey and you shall have your reward.'

He put his hand out to her and said, 'Come, Mary, let me show you something.'

She made herself take his hand and the palm of it was hard and dry.

He led her to one of the walls. He pressed a panel. A secret door opened showing a winding staircase. As they climbed it she could smell the sweat on him and was almost sick. It had been a day of smells, all of them foul. If there was one great distinction between the Scottish court and the French, it was that the French court was scented to the nose. At the top of the staircase he pressed another panel and they stepped into her apartment. Her four ladies were laying out her clothes, but this was not what took her eye.

The room and its furnishings were exactly as her bedroom had been in the château in France. She gasped and tears pricked her eyes. Her familiar things of silver and gold, the tapestries, the candlebra, the cabinets, the bed, all stood there. She could hardly bring herself to speak because suddenly she wanted to weep and knew she must not do so in front of her brother. Her ladies curtsied to her and Stuart said, 'Here is your bedchamber. I persuaded your uncle, the Cardinal, to permit me to bring from France all your personal belongings.'

'I do thank you for that,' she said softly. 'I thank you with all my heart.'

He led her from the bedchamber. The door to the turret chamber was filled by a tapestry which he lifted so that she could walk through.

'And here,' he said, 'you will dine and take your ease.'

She saw it was a narrow room, and there sat Riccio. He had changed his clothes. He bowed and smiled, struck some preliminary chords on his guitar and then sang.

All men rejoice
That you are safely come
To grace with beauty your new realm.
Spring blossoms in your smile
Where lately winter froze the heart,
And few there are
That see upon your perfect cheek
A crystal tear
Like dew upon the petalled rose.
Do not lament, sweet Queen,
Your passing from fair France which cherished you.
Rejoice!
For you have come
To grace with beauty your new realm.

The third room of her royal apartments at Holyrood was the presence chamber. She saw that it had a door to the bedroom as well as the turret chamber. James indicated the throne on the dais.

'If you will prepare yourself, in an hour I will bring all the Lords of Scotland to you and present them.'

He turned to take his leave and saw Ballard in one corner of the room watching them.

44

He said sharply, 'Stay out of the public eye, priest, and do not provoke the lords. There will be a private chapel for your religion.'

He went to the main door which connected the apartments to the rest of the palace and he was struck by another thought.

'And you, Mary, may travel if you choose. Scotland is a fine land.'

Mary seemed overcome with gratitude and she smiled and said, 'Thank you, dear brother.'

'Dear sister.'

The French guards closed the door behind him. Mary ran into the turret room. She could no longer contain herself. She began to weep with anger. Riccio rose in alarm.

'I am trapped,' she sobbed. 'I am trapped.'

Riccio, no longer the smiling musician, said firmly, 'Not yet, your grace.'

'But he has me in a cage.'

'Then you must appear to sing sweetly and happily.'

'I cannot. I cannot. The lies stick in my throat. It took all my power to smile at him. I hate him. I cannot go on with it.'

'He is learning to trust you.'

'What difference can that make? He rules here.'

'When he trusts you he will become careless and then you will have him in a cage.'

'Davie,' she said desperately, 'I have no army. No Treasury. No allies. Even Bothwell has gone.'

'That is not true,' said Riccio. 'You have allies. The Pope is first among them, then your uncles.'

Ballard, who had come to the door of the turret room, said firmly, 'That is true. You have allies.'

'He patronized me as if I were a foolish girl. I am the Queen.'

'In name only until you marry,' replied Ballard.

'No,' she wept, 'I still mourn my poor Francis.'

'We must find you a husband,' said Riccio calmly.

'A Catholic,' said Ballard, 'with an army at his back to deal with the good James Stuart, and then you will march South. Do not forget that, madam.'

Riccio was irritated. 'First, let us secure Scotland.'

Mary stopped crying. 'Is it possible?'

'It is certain.'

Mary turned to Ballard. 'And the English throne? Shall I gain it?'

Ballard said with the absolute certainty of a fanatic, 'It is yours by right, so it will be yours. God is not mocked.'

Then I must marry quickly, she thought. I will not drag out my days in this cold and barren land. She shivered and said, 'Did you look upon the grim and ragged people as we rode today? Did you smell those fine Scottish lords? Mother of God. To think that my sweet mother endured all this for my sake. All those years of my happiness and luxury in France she was here among these savages. I am ashamed of my tears. Today I leave childhood behind. Yes, I will marry as you say.'

Riccio smiled and said, 'It shall be our policy.'

She smiled back, wiping the tears from her face. Riccio thought, how good it is to be only eighteen years old; hope rises quickly.

'So it shall, so it shall Davie,' she smiled. 'Let us begin at once.'

She shouted, 'Mary Seton! Mary Seton!'

Seton came running from the bedroom with a dress in her hand.

'Madam?'

'Paper, Mary, and ink and a sander, seals and quills and a penknife. Davie, where is your room?'

Riccio was shocked.

'You must not be seen with me.'

Mary cut in imperiously, 'Come, come, come, come, come.'

46

She ran into the bedroom, knocking over a dress-stand on her way to open the panel in the wall.

'There!' she said in triumph.

'Ah,' said Riccio, and he was delighted.

'I can come to you when I please,' said Mary, 'we will work in your chamber daily.'

'No,' said Ballard.

'Yes, I say. No one will suspect.'

'Your grace, if they do they will find a very evil reason for your action. Believe me a queen may not consort with a commoner in secret.'

Seton brought the silver casket. Mary took it and for a moment she was sad. She traced the letters on the lid with her finger. They were intertwined – 'F' and 'M'. Poor Francis, poor Francis. And she remembered the day when he gave it to her. She opened the lid and inside were all her writing materials.

Riccio said, 'It is you who must decide, your grace.'

'Yes I must,' she replied turning to her confessor. 'What would seem worse, Father, if it comes to it – that I am suspected of visiting a musician or that he is suspected of visiting me? It must be one or other if Davie is to write my secret letters and code them and bring me the replies. So I will decide – for, at least among my only loyal subjects,' she laughed for a moment and indicated them, the four ladies-in-waiting, the priest and the little Italian, 'and in my own tiny kingdom,' she indicated the apartment, 'I will be Queen.'

'*Bravissimo*,' said Riccio.

'Hurry, hurry,' said Mary. 'I will not waste a second.'

She was hurrying through and onto the spiral staircase before Ballard could protest. Riccio followed and closed the door.

CHAPTER FOUR

So began Mary's secret correspondence with the Pope, Philip of Spain, and her uncles in France. In London Elizabeth, who also tantalized and rejected suitors, heard of it and acted. She was in residence at Whitehall when she ordered the attendance of the ambassadors of France and Spain, Austria, and Scotland. For once she was sorry that there was no representative from the Pope in England, so that she might also tell him what she had in her mind.

They were splendidly dressed to attend her. The styles of their beards were as assorted as their hats. They strode, hands on sword hilts, cloaks trailing, along the gallery between the Queen's guard of halberdiers. The doors of the presence chamber swung open and they hurried in. They arranged themselves at a distance from one another, fussing with their cloaks and jewel chains until at last the trumpets sounded. They bowed. The doors from the council chamber opened and Elizabeth entered. She, too, was elaborately dressed, and accompanied by a resplendent Dudley.

She said in French to the French ambassador, 'Welcome, your excellency. I believe the Queen Regent is well?'

And to the Spaniard in Castilian Spanish, 'The noble Philip constantly inspires me with his dedication to his realm, ambassador.'

To the Austrian she said in German, 'The Archduke Charles is so handsome in his portrait that I long to see the original, my lord.'

To the Scottish ambassador she said, and her tone was cooler, 'My lord ambassador it is to you, above all, that I shall speak today for your mistress, the gracious Queen of Scots, is the subject of this happy meeting.'

She seated herself on her throne. They waited. She seemed to be considering how she should put it to them. In a friendly voice she said at last, 'Your excellency, Mary Stuart plans to marry.'

The ambassadors were shaken. Did she know of the long and flattering letters written by Riccio to Philip of Spain suggesting that Mary should marry his imbecile son Don Carlos? Or, in another direction, letters which encouraged the Cardinal to suggest to Catherine that Mary marry Charles, the young brother of the dead Francis? The Austrian ambassador wondered if Cecil's spies had intercepted his diplomatic bag and read the letters which suggested that the Archduke Charles would be very happy to marry the beautiful Mary. An awkward situation, as he was also negotiating to marry Elizabeth.

Elizabeth allowed their unease to come to full flower before she continued. 'No one in the universe,' she said affably, 'can better understand than you, my lords, who spend your lives in diplomacy, that the marriage plans of our dear cousin in Scotland are very close to our heart.'

Yes, thought the Scottish ambassador, and there are no lengths to which you will not go to prevent her having a Catholic husband of royal blood.

'In particular,' she went on, 'we believe you will understand that if Mary attempts to marry the French Charles, the Spanish Don Carlos or the Austrian Charles her action will be treated as an act of war against England.'

They began to protest and she raised her hand. They were silent.

'We realize,' she said so graciously that it put their teeth on edge, 'that our sweet young cousin has been deluded by dangerous and self-seeking men. We are not angry. We desire nothing more than her happiness, her safety and a suitable marriage. So we offer now a wise and just solution.'

She rose and held out her hand at full stretch and Dudley, taking his cue, moved to her to kiss it.

'We offer,' she said, 'our most loyal and loving subject, Lord Robert Dudley, to Mary Stuart in marriage.'

The Scottish ambassador almost shouted no. But fortunately for him he held his tongue.

'And,' she went on, 'we shall tomorrow create him Earl of Leicester, that he is the more worthy.'

She took her hand from Dudley's, patted his cheek and then, turning, she left the presence chamber, the guards hurriedly opening the doors into the council chamber before her and Dudley following her two paces behind. As the doors were closing he turned and bowed ironically to the ambassadors. When the doors were safely shut there was uproar.

In the council chamber Cecil was waiting for them. The sound of outrage came faintly through the heavy doors.

Elizabeth, who ate little and slept less, seemed this morning to be in radiant health. She said, 'I am very hungry.'

Immediately servants went to bring food to her. She sat at the council table. Cecil inclined his head towards Dudley.

'She will not take him. She will rage against the insult.'

He indicated the sounds that still came through the door, 'As they do.'

Dudley replied, 'It is not my choice to go North to that barbarous land.'

'It is mine,' said Elizabeth fondly.

Cecil eased his painful leg and Elizabeth said, 'Sit, please sit, my old friend.'

As he did so, Cecil said, 'He is a commoner, a Protestant, and the subject of both scandal and rumour.'

'My choice.'

Dudley smiled. 'My lord,' he said, 'I shall obey with a better heart knowing that I am opposed by you.'

Cecil replied mildly, 'You are not suitable. I must say it. My duty is to foresee the result of English policy and convince the Queen.'

'What you judge ill for me must benefit me. That is the lesson of our past dealings.'

Servants entered and placed the food in front of Elizabeth who began to eat at once. She said, between mouthfuls, 'And you can feel a crown.'

She put out a free hand and pointed to his head, 'There.'

Dudley protested, 'It is you I love. Only you.'

'Then marry Mary, for only when she is married to a loving subject of mine will I be safe from the assassin, the fanatic and the rebellion in her cause.'

Elizabeth anticipated Cecil's next objection. 'And she will take him because with him I will send the thing she most lusts after – the promise, sealed and witnessed, of the English throne at my death.'

Cecil became very stern.

'Madam, you cannot give that promise. Neither Parliament nor the people will sanction it. She is a Catholic and we will never again have a Catholic monarch in this land.'

'I will do it in secret. I and my people will live out my reign in peace and prosperity. Safe, because my good lord here, putting aside personal ambitions, will forgo England and his beloved Queen, marry Mary and govern all in Scotland.'

'I will,' said Dudley fervently as if at that moment he were kneeling with Mary before the altar. 'I will.'

Elizabeth went on, 'And the Scottish Queen, freed from the tyranny of the dour James Stuart, will live happily for the certain day when she, and then her heir, will rule these British Isles.'

'Madam,' said Cecil, 'this is inept policy. She will refuse him and throughout Europe you will be a laughing stock. You lay yourself open to insult and rebuff.'

'No, no,' said Elizabeth. 'I believe I know her better than you.'

She turned to Dudley.

51

'Go now, begin your preparations, Robin, for the ceremony tomorrow and the journey afterwards. Go quickly before my heart betrays me.'

Dudley was visibly moved by this and he kissed her hand passionately.

'Sweet Majesty,' he said, 'sweet Majesty.'

And he hurried from the room to hide his emotions. When the door closed behind him Elizabeth leaned back from the food and she laughed out loud at Cecil. Cecil looked sternly back at her.

'Your Majesty,' he said, 'you will regret this day, and if you think Robert Dudley will ever put aside his ambition —'

Elizabeth interrupted him. 'Do you really believe that she will not take him?'

'I do,'

'Good,' said Elizabeth. 'Excellent. For I do not intend her to have him.'

God save us, thought Cecil. Now where will she lead us all?

Elizabeth indicated the door to the presence chamber with the knife she was holding.

'But I mean the world to think that I do. Within three days every Catholic court in Europe will have the news, and tomorrow we will make the most of the ceremony when I create the good and faithful Robin Earl of Leicester. All ambassadors will be there. I shall even disgrace myself a little before them by my intimacy with the new Earl. All this will be reported most faithfully to Mary Stuart. She will die rather than have him.'

'But *why*?' said Cecil, 'What can you gain by this?'

She told him.

It was cold in the Tower of London that winter. The bitter winds that blew from the North Sea entered every crack, crevice and window. In his cell Bothwell ached with the cold. The rain was so heavy that half the land was covered with ice where it froze as it fell. It was so cold that birds fell out of the sky and from trees with their wings frozen. The edge of the sea froze along the east coast and blizzards blocked the roads to Berwick and the North. From his cell window in the day Bothwell could see people walking across the fast-frozen Thames. His food was poor. He had very little money left. He did not know that Mary had written to Elizabeth a cordial letter attempting his release. She wrote: *Excellent high and mighty princess, our dearest sister and cousin, we most earnestly desire if it please you that you would grant liberty to the Earl Bothwell so that he may leave your land.*

Elizabeth did not reply because the letter never reached her. It was intercepted. As Cecil put it to the candle flame he heard the voice of James Stuart on the day when they had made the plan to seize Bothwell's ship. 'He is the most dangerous of men and he has a history which in itself is a bad omen. Both his father and his grandfather nearly married a queen of Scotland. With him to help her Mary might find the way to rule Scotland and imperil the Protestant cause in both our lands. He and I are enemies. It is well concealed, but enemies we are in the blood. When it comes to it, in the end one of us must finish the other.'

Cecil was unimpressed. 'He is not a Papist,' he said. That was his yardstick. Either a man was an enemy which meant he was a Papist, or he was a friend which meant he was a Protestant. His words echoed those of Ballard who had spoken of two sorts of men. James Stuart was surprised by this response and said, 'He is worse, surely you know. He cares nothing for either cause. He is an atheist and he cannot be bribed.'

'Cannot be bribed?' Cecil was amazed because every man had his price and it was not unusual for a good loyal servant of the Queen to take a Spanish pension.

'Not even,' said James Stuart to rub it in, 'with English gold my lord.'

'Well, well,' said Cecil. 'I have never met such a man to my knowledge. I hope we may take him alive.'

'Alive or dead you must take him,' said James, 'his loyalty is to the Stuarts. It is his pride and Mary is the last Stuart.'

The thaw had set in. For a week it rained day and night outside his cell window. Although it was after midnight Bothwell was awake to hear, above the sound of the rain, feet approaching along the stone corridor; then the key in the lock and the bolt being drawn. The cell door was pushed open. He was dazzled by the light of lanterns. He sat up with his back against the wall. One guard with a lantern entered the cell. Beyond him he could just discern a dim figure of middle height outlined against a second lantern outside. Cecil stepped into the light in the cell.

'Leave the lantern,' he said to the guard, 'and get out. Do not bolt the door.'

The guard left the cell. Cecil stood leaning on his stick.

'Good sir,' he said, 'I am told that you are a man who cannot be bought.'

'And you,' said Bothwell, who was sitting up, 'you are Cecil. You give gold to Scottish traitors.'

Cecil said thoughtfully as if he had just received the news that minute, 'And you are quite penniless because the Lord James Stuart has sold all your lands in your absence. And further, you may remain here until your death. You have no friends. No man will ransom you. A sad fate for such a daring lord.'

Amiably Bothwell replied, 'I have long had it in mind to kill you, Master Cecil.'

'Ah,' said Cecil. 'And I have it in mind to release you.'

'What is the price?'

'There is no price,' said Cecil. 'And the rest will be explained to you by someone more able than I. Come.'

Bothwell eased his aching bones off the bed.

While they waited for the tide to turn and carry them

back up the river to Whitehall, Bothwell trimmed his beard, washed, changed into a fine suit of clothes which Cecil had thoughtfully provided, and was glad to have back his sword and dagger. They wrapped their cloaks round them and went out of the Tower, down the steps to the landing stage and into the boat. An hour later they entered the palace at Whitehall by a side door. When they came to the Queen's apartments the candles were alight. The women had been sent away and Elizabeth herself was welcoming.

'My lord,' she said, 'I have long wanted to meet you.'

'And I you, madam,' said Bothwell looking at her and thinking, she has the eyes of a great cat. The nose is too long. The hands are beautiful. There are more jewels in that dress than I have seen in a lifetime.

She offered him wine. She showed him her apartments. Eventually she took him to a small ornamented desk. Cecil, nearby, was holding a candlebra so that the light might fall on the contents. She took out two small objects wrapped in paper. She allowed him to see, as if by accident, that written on one paper in her own fine hand were the words 'My Lord's Picture'. She unwrapped the miniature of Dudley and she said wistfully, 'I am loathe to part with my lord's picture.'

'But you have the original,' said Bothwell helpfully, wondering what all this was leading to.

Elizabeth did not reply. She was unwrapping the second. It was of Mary. Apparently impulsively she kissed it and then placed it beside the miniature of Dudley.

'How well they go together,' she said. 'If your sweet mistress is wise she will have both this little picture and the original.'

Then she told him that to show her good-will and her complete openness in the matter she was releasing him from the Tower to return to Scotland and be her secret ambassador to Mary.

'You must know, my lord,' she said, 'that above all men I respect the lord whose loyalty to his Queen is unwavering and I know that you cannot be bribed or seduced from your allegiance to Mary.'

She touched his hand briefly and he thought, if Cecil were not here, by God, I believe I could tumble her. She's bony for my taste but she would be spirited.

Elizabeth had taken something else from the desk. It was a document.

'Read this,' she said. He read it and he was amazed. In her own hand Elizabeth promised Mary of Scotland the throne of England. She named her the true and only heir and successor. When he got to the end of it he said, 'But it is not signed, your grace.'

'It will be,' she said, 'when Mary takes the Earl of Leicester in marriage.'

Bothwell looked from her to Cecil. No, he thought, the wily fox and old Harry's daughter have something else in mind. They seemed disappointed by his silence.

'My lord,' said Elizabeth, 'your only duty to me, to earn your freedom, is to tell Mary that my offer is sincere, and that you have met me and spoken to me and know me to be honest.'

'That,' lied Bothwell, 'I can do.'

'Further,' said Elizabeth, 'all this must be in the deepest secrecy. The proposal that your mistress should be made the heir to this throne is as hateful to my Parliament and people as it is to the party of Lord James Stuart in Scotland. I am therefore as much in your hands as you are in mine.'

'It shall be kept secret,' he said doing his best to give an impression of sober integrity.

Cecil, who had been waiting for this moment, said gravely, 'To convince you of our honesty you must know that we would never have taken your ship had not the Lord James Stuart visited us on his journey back to Scotland from France.'

'Ah,' said Bothwell, 'so that was it.'

Elizabeth said, 'We do not fear your influence with Mary, but he does.'

Bothwell laughed out loud. They want James Stuart destroyed. That's what they're after.

'Trust me,' he said. 'I shall be happy to be your ambassador in secret; and this document' – he held up the promise of succession – 'I will present with my own hands in secret to my Queen.'

'Excellent,' said Cecil. 'And now you must rest before the journey.'

As he was going Elizabeth said as an afterthought.

'There is one other small matter. Mary Stuart and I have in common a cousin by blood, Henry, Lord Darnley. He will accompany you. It is he who in public will present gifts, and my personal greetings, to your sovereign. He is a most dazzling and accomplished courtier and will take the eye from you. In due time – when you have spoken to the Queen – the Earl of Leicester will follow you to Scotland.'

Bothwell thought, send who you like but just let me get my foot on Scottish soil again.

Henry Stuart, Lord Darnley, dressed in white and gold, mounted on the finest of Mary's six white horses, rode ahead of the other five each carrying a groom of the royal household. The ground was sodden underfoot and the hooves of the horses sank into the turf.

In an age when most men grew a beard or a moustache Darnley had neither and was thought by some to be ladyfaced. Elizabeth, mounted, with Cecil by her side, looked at him with intense satisfaction as he approached. He was tall, handsome and arrogant. Skilful at dancing and at music, he could also write a charming verse, flatter, or speak with a sharp and wicked wit according to the occasion.

There was a break in the lowering grey skies and a thin shaft of sun came through to shine on Darnley and his party.

Elizabeth was apparently so pleased with the sight that she cried out, 'God give you a good journey, my lord.'

Darnley bowed in the saddle.

'I charge you,' she said affectionately, 'to tell the Queen it is our deepest shame that these fine horses were taken in error. Say to her that Elizabeth most abjectly begs her forgiveness.'

'Trust me, your grace.'

'I do, good Henry,' she said warmly, 'I trust you to fulfil all my hopes. And treat those beasts well on the journey. I would not have them arrive at her court in less fine condition than they are now.'

Bothwell, who had been waiting a discreet distance behind the Queen, rode forward and said, 'I'll see to them. It was my charge in France and I will complete it.'

'I'll wager you,' she murmured as they began their ride North, 'fifty pounds that she will take him.'

Cecil was almost as mean about money as Elizabeth, and more cautious with age. Sanctimoniously he said, 'Madam, it is too serious a matter for gambling.'

'She is a young widow. The blood is hot. When that young man rides into her court she will look upon him –' Elizabeth paused, and then she made it sound as blatantly lecherous as she could in order to embarrass her puritan minister – 'in the flesh with great favour, and he will be there before Robin.'

'I am uneasy,' said Cecil, trying to hide his dislike of the bawdy side of the Queen's nature, 'I do not believe that any true monarch would ignore the offer of the succession, and for that she must take Leicester.'

Elizabeth pulled on a rein and began to walk her horse.

'That monarch,' she said, 'is first a woman.'

'Ha!' said Cecil in triumph. 'That is my point. You, too, are a woman but you would never ignore a crown for that pretty fellow.'

Elizabeth replied sharply, 'This woman is first a monarch.'

Soon it was the turn of Dudley to be God-sped to the North. As he rode up to the Queen and Cecil she said loudly, 'God give the new Earl of Leicester a good journey.'

Dressed in black and scarlet, the magnificent new Earl bowed from the saddle of his favourite horse.

'I thank you, your grace.'

'The whole court,' said Elizabeth excessively, 'will pray that your wooing pleases the lady.'

Leicester looked into the eyes of his mistress, his expression boyish and eager.

'You may depend upon it, madam.'

For a moment Elizabeth turned her head from him and he thought, how she will miss me. It had not occurred to him that she might be hiding laughter. She turned back pink-cheeked and said, 'Tell the sweet Queen that I believe a marriage will settle all our differences. Now ride on, my faithful subject, and fulfil my hopes.'

Dudley and his entourage set off at a sharp canter. Cecil brought his horse close to Elizabeth who seemed absorbed in this brave show.

'Now I am certain,' he said complacently. 'No woman would choose the boy before the man. I will accept your wager. Fifty pounds that she takes Leicester and the succession.'

Elizabeth was no longer smiling.

'If she takes Robin,' she said coldly, 'then we are safe but I have paid a price for it. But if she takes the other as I believe she will then we have given nothing and,' – her voice was now so full of hatred that the hairs lifted on the nape of Cecil's neck, – 'she has a weak and degenerate fool without power or influence as her consort. Win or lose the wager, Master Cecil, I cannot lose the game.'

CHAPTER FIVE

On a morning of false spring which briefly broke the grip of winter two horses raced along the sands at Leith. The tide ran strongly into the Firth of Forth; and a warm wind, west against the tide, lifted small white caps to cheer the eye in the unexpected sunshine. The fishing vessels were out and the scavenging gulls swooped and cried in the wake of them.

At a distance both riders appeared to be men. But one of them was Mary Stuart dressed in clothes identical to those of Darnley who raced against her. The two white horses seemed to fly, their manes and tails streaming in the wind, and it seemed to Mary they could go on like that, in a kind of ecstasy, to the world's end.

The ecstasy had begun on a Sunday morning. Mary, her servants and her ladies were in the small chapel royal to attend Mass. Servants, under the instruction of Ballard, were placing the altar candles and ornaments when from outside the chapel door came the first sound of a mob. Voices shouted for blood; for the death of the priest; for the destruction of all filthy Papists and idolaters; for the casting down of the ornaments and the destruction of the candles. Fists hammered the chapel door. Bodies were hurled against it.

There was no other way out. Ballard and the servants placed themselves between the door and the Queen and her ladies and waited for the worst. As the frenzy increased and the hinges splintered Mary suddenly heard hooves on the cobbles as horses galloped past the altar end of the chapel. Outside the mob scattered as Bothwell and Darnley and their servants rode them down. They broke in all directions, beaten with the flat of swords and heavy pistol butts. Now there were cries and moans as those with broken heads and bones were dragged away by their fellows. Bothwell dismounted, and going to the chapel door called out, 'It is I, the Lord Bothwell. You can open up.'

Ballard opened the door and Bothwell entered to kneel to his Queen.

Darnley dismounted. A man moaning on the ground with a smashed thigh turned towards him and raised a hand as if to plead for help. Darnley poised his sword for the thrust, enjoyed the terror in the man's eyes, then passed the sword through him, killing him instantly. He wiped the sword on the dead man's clothes, sheathed it and went into the chapel.

He heard Bothwell saying, 'They seem to hate your priest madam,' and Mary replying with spirit, 'As much as I hate John Knox, my lord.'

In that moment she looked past Bothwell and she saw him. He was a head taller than most men and because she, herself, was very tall, her first surprise was that here was a man she had to look up to. But more than that, it was as if a young god from antiquity had appeared. He was goldenhaired, beautiful and smooth of face, strong in proportion to his height, long-legged and unlike any man she had met in her life. With an easy grace he moved to her, bowed and said, 'Your Majesty?'

He kissed her hand.

'I have come from England to return the horses that were stolen and bring you the greetings of Elizabeth, my Queen.'

'Who are you?' said Mary.

'I am your cousin Henry Stuart, Lord Darnley.'

'You are most welcome, cousin.'

She felt herself shaking. He smiled and, unlike so many of those who surrounded her, all his teeth were sound and white and his breath was sweet.

'It is my good fortune,' he said, 'to have come at this moment to defend your person and our Church.'

Bothwell said abruptly, 'I will return your horses to the stables, madam.'

She neither heard nor saw him. He left.

Mary said, 'Our Church?'

'Yes.'

'Then, cousin,' she said joyfully, 'let us take the comfortable sacrament together and give thanks for your arrival and my deliverance this day.'

'With all my heart.'

Ballard closed the doors of the chapel himself and walked to the altar. When he saw them kneeling together, for no good reason that he could think of, his heart was troubled.

On the sands Darnley's horse stumbled and he fell. She was ten yards past him before she finally brought her horse to a halt and turned back to him. He lay stunned. She dropped on her knees by him and began to weep. She was terrified that he was dead. Involuntarily she said, 'Harry, my love, my love,' and put a hand out to touch his head.

He stirred. She took a scarf from her neck, ran to a rock pool and soaked it in the water, and then ran back to him, panting and weeping. Darnley tried to sit up. She controlled her emotions.

'Be still.'

She bathed his head. Darnley, looking up at her, could not at first focus on her face. He managed to say, 'What a happy fall to have such comfort afterwards.'

She did not trust herself to reply. He said, 'There are tears on your cheeks,' and he sat up.

She was conscious of the wet sand pressing up through the hose into her legs and of the smell of seaweed, of the wind on her face, and, above all, of the dangerous closeness of Darnley. Miles of empty sand stretched beyond them on either side. Now, she thought and felt faint, – now?

She heard herself reply coldly, 'I saw again the death of my husband, that is all.'

She moved abruptly away to the horses. Despite the pain in his head Darnley was overjoyed and he wondered how soon he dare bring matters to a conclusion.

Elizabeth was in residence at Greenwich. It was the palace she loved above all the others. The palace where she had been born; where her mother, Anne Boleyn, whose name she never mentioned, had been happy. It was the palace nearest the sea and it fronted the broad sweep of the Thames where all vessels coming up to the port of London could be seen as they went by.

She slept better at Greenwich than anywhere else, so when the doors of her bedchamber were abruptly opened in the small hours of the morning, she woke up in a fury that anyone had dared to disturb her. There stood Dudley, weather-stained from hard riding and in a towering rage which he had managed to sustain through four days' journey. Behind him she saw the attendants and guards who were terrified to lay a hand on him and equally terrified of the wrath she would visit on them for permitting this unpardonable intrusion. There was a moment of complete silence.

Icily she said, 'Well, Robin?'

He slammed the doors behind him. In a tone almost of high tragedy he said, 'I am rejected, she rejected me.'

Elizabeth had to hide her face in her hands not to laugh out loud and Dudley took this reaction to be shock which encouraged him to pour out his sorrows.

'She kept me waiting for five days without an audience,' he exclaimed. 'She flaunted herself before me in the company of Darnley. She dines with Darnley. She dances with Darnley. She rides with Darnley.'

'And has rejected you,' said Elizabeth, expressionless.

'With insults,' said Leicester. 'She was encouraged to it by Bothwell, your honest messenger, madam. She spoke of me openly as your cast-off lover and far beneath any true queen in station. Is she demented? Is she possessed by evil spirits that wish to destroy her? Before my eyes she tore up the document of succession.'

'Ah,' said Elizabeth. She was almost choking with the fierce pleasure of her triumph.

'Believe me, madam,' said Leicester, 'I understand your disappointment. She consorts only with that boy. That mincing, lewd, lisping, pouting boy and she rejects me. And, by God, she has seen me. She has seen the man before her and, by all the saints, madam, she is a woman that needs a man.'

It was very unwise of him. Elizabeth was instantly alert to rivalry. When she replied her tone was deceptively mild.

'What kind of a woman, Robin?'

Dudley, wholly concerned with himself and his humiliation, said, 'Formed like a goddess.'

'How formed like a goddess?'

'Tall, graceful, curved as a woman should be.'

Suddenly his energy seemed to leave him and he sighed for the loss of it. All that and two kingdoms. It was enough to depress a man and indeed to make him less aware than usual of the look in Elizabeth's eye.

Elizabeth pressed him, 'More than I? Is she better formed than I?'

'No, no, madam,' he said absently.

'Does she dance more elegantly?'

'No, but with a certain fire.'

'She is fiery?' said Elizabeth as if politely surprised. 'I had heard that she is dull and sits by the hour sewing. Does she play instruments more skilfully than I?'

'No,' said Dudley encouraged by her kind interest, 'but to do her justice she loves music.'

The explosion was not far off.

'Can she speak freely in German, Italian, Latin and Greek as I can?'

'Who knows,' he said, 'But she speaks most sweetly and with a charming accent.'

Elizabeth suddenly shouted, 'She charmed you. This woman who has offered me the most deadly insult charms you, my lord.'

Too late he realized and said, 'No, I found her tiresome.'

'Liar!' shouted Elizabeth and she jumped from the bed and threw a shoe at him. Then she ran at him and struck him with all her strength across the face twice. She did it with all the power and venom of which she was capable and he staggered back.

'You,' she said savagely, 'were as eager as a young lover to ride to her, to wed her and bed her.'

'I love you only.'

'You're a vulgar, strutting fool,' she shouted.

He said, unable to do any better, 'It was a sacrifice for England.'

She promptly hit him again.

'Liar!'

There was a panting pause.

'Well,' she said, 'I cannot complain. You have played your part.'

He was alert and said, 'My part?'

She changed the subject at once.

'It is her loss that she rejects you.'

She touched his cheek where she had struck him.

'And how glad I am to have you home.'

She put her arms round his neck and kissed him full on the lips. With her face against his she murmured, 'Is she as beautiful as they say. Answer truly for I am no longer angry with you.'

Over her shoulder Dudley looked longingly at the bed which he hoped to be in within the next few moments.

'Well,' he said reluctantly, 'she is quite beautiful.'

And then he began to embrace her.

'My love,' he said, 'my love.'

In an outburst that left no doubt that she was the daughter of the great Henry and that one part of her character was as vain and unpredictable and violent as her father's, she pulled clear of him and screamed, 'Out! Out! Out! Do not dare to speak of her beauty, you clod. God's death I have it in me to send you to cool your passion for her beauty in the Tower. Out! Get out!'

He turned and almost ran from her as she struck at him. The door closed and she stood panting with her back against it. She whispered a prayer, 'May it please Almighty God that she hates me as I do her for then she must marry the Lord Darnley and I have won.'

Darnley lay naked upon the bed and gazed lazily around the chamber. In the sleepy aftermath of lovemaking, what he saw pleased him. There were rich hangings. At least a dozen swords with jewelled hilts in rich scabbards hung on one wall. Gorgeous suits of clothes, hung upon clothes-horses which stood like spectators round the room. Finally there beside him was his loved one.

He said, 'You are becoming too rich, Davie.'

Riccio smiled. 'I am valued.'

'No,' said Darnley to provoke him, 'You are hated.'

'Not by you, sweet Harry.'

Darnley needled away at him, 'The commoner, the upstart, the detested little foreigner.'

'Ah, you are jealous of my influence. Shall I give you some of the presents that the good nobles offer me? They know that to find their way into the Queen's favour they must first find the favour of the Queen's secretary.'

'They only do that until they can find a way to finish you.'

'Not while the Queen lives.'

Darnley raised himself on one elbow and spoke seriously, 'That is as true for me as for others. You must speak for me Davie. I will be king here.'

Riccio turned his back on him and said, 'If God wills it. Now go to sleep.'

Darnley lost his temper. 'Why do you put me off?'

Without turning his head Riccio mumbled, 'Policy.'

'What policy? I have the right to be a king. All the Catholic nobles of England will support Mary's cause if I am king.'

Riccio turned back to him, 'But you are vicious, Harry. You have a taste for all the vices.'

'I thought you loved me.'

Riccio looked at him steadily. 'I love the Queen better and I think it a cruel act to help to put you between her sheets.'

'You want to keep me between yours.'

Riccio laughed. 'Edinburgh is full of pretty boys, as you know, and like you I have a taste for a woman as well. I shall not lack for comfort, Harry, if you come no more to my bed – so cool your anger. The truth is that we are both outcasts in this court. No man is your friend save me and no man is mine save you. Like it nor not Harry we must hold to each other.'

There was a knock on the door. A very sharp rap that made them both start. A servant's voice said, 'Señor Riccio, the Queen is coming.'

'The Queen!'

They both got out of bed in near panic. Darnley rapidly picked up his clothes which were scattered across the floor and ran naked through a door in a curtained alcove. Riccio put on a dressing-gown and looked quickly round to see that there was no evidence of Darnley's presence. He closed the curtain across the alcove and by the time there was another knock on the door he was laying out paper and quills and wax on the table. He sat quill in hand and then called, 'Enter.'

The door was opened for Mary by his Italian servant. As

she pushed back the hood of her cloak he could see that her hair was down. Riccio rose to greet her.

'Working,' said Mary affectionately. 'Always working.'

'I could not sleep.'

'Nor I, nor I, Davie. You must advise me.'

'If I can, your grace.'

She began to pace up and down the chamber.

'If I marry a foreign Catholic prince there will be war with England.'

'Yes.'

'But if I marry a Catholic Englishman?'

Playing for time Riccio said carefully, 'Must it be marriage, your grace?'

'What?' said Mary not understanding, 'what do you say?'

He said bluntly, 'Elizabeth does well without marriage and she is mistress of all things in her land.'

Mary was shocked and outraged.

'That strumpet. She is a whore. The daughter of a witch and a foul lecher who cast down our Church. Davie, you shame me. I will take no lovers.'

'Forgive me.'

It is hard to believe, he thought, that she was brought up in the French court. It may well be that angels stand at the four corners of her bed but that is no help to me in framing policy in this treacherous age.

'You must answer me, Davie,' she commanded. 'Is the Lord Darnley a good match? Would the Holy Father and Philip of Spain give their blessing to it?'

'I cannot deny it.'

She seemed overjoyed at this unenthusiastic reply. 'I knew it. I believe it is God's will that both wise policy and my deepest longings are fulfilled in him because I love him.'

'Yes,' he said. 'I see you do, your grace.'

'I've been very lonely,' she said. 'From the day poor Francis died until Lord Darnley came to my court I did not care whether I lived or died. Now I am so full of joy I dare hardly speak in his presence for fear I shall tell him of my great love. It is the good fortune of queens to choose where other women must wait to be chosen. I choose him, Davie. He will be my husband, my lover and my companion.'

Riccio made a last attempt. 'Your grace, I would sacrifice my life for your happiness. But I must ask you this – will you accept the Lord Darnley as your master if you make him the king in this land?'

Mary completely misunderstood him and said, 'Davie, Davie, do not fear that you will be displaced. Is that why you are so grudging in your answers?'

'It is not for me I fear, but for you.'

'I shall be first in the realm. I am the Queen. He will understand that if he loves me. Dare I hope that he loves me? You must speak for me, Davie. You must find out. I must say nothing until I am certain.'

Riccio inclined his head but did not reply. She was struck by another thought and said, 'Will the Scottish lords hate him?'

And Riccio said dryly, 'No more than any other foreigner set over them.'

There was a long pause; she continued to walk up and down the room and he watched her.

She said with finality, 'I must have him. Pray for me.'

Then she laughed out loud at the thought of it.

'Oh what a fine king he will make.'

Impulsively she bent to kiss Riccio on the cheek.

'It is wonderful to be so happy and so certain. Pray for me. Goodnight, Davie.'

Riccio listened for the outer door to close then he went to the curtain in the alcove and pulled it aside. The door beyond was shut. He opened it and called, 'Harry. Are you there?'

He was pouring wine when Darnley, in hose and shirt and shoes, carrying his doublet, belt and dagger, came back into the room. Darnley threw his gear down and said suspiciously, 'Does she often visit you at night, Davie?'

'We have to work here in secret.'

'Is it only matters of State that she came for?'

Riccio handed him a glass of wine.

'You have the mind of a brothel-keeper. Didn't you listen at the door to find out?'

'I listened but the curtain was too thick.'

'Before she came,' said Riccio, 'you wanted me to speak for you.'

'Yes.'

'If I did, and it seemed that she would love you and take you to husband, would you give her first place acknowledging her true monarch of this realm?'

Darnley finished his wine.

'No,' he said confidently, 'I will be master.'

'Then I will oppose you.'

Darnley began to laugh. He could no longer keep the joke to himself. Mockingly he repeated Mary's words. ' "I am so full of joy. I dare hardly speak in his presence for I fear I shall tell him of my great love." The curtain is so thick, Davie, I was forced to open the door and step into the room to hear clearly. When will she find the courage to ask me? Will it be tomorrow?'

Riccio did not accept defeat. He said sharply, 'Do not betray her. I warn you for your sake. Treat her lovingly.'

'Speak gently to your King, Master Riccio. Do not threaten.'

Riccio said angrily, 'You have two kingdoms in your grasp —'

But before he could go on Darnley shouted, 'I drink to my kingdoms.'

He seized the flask of wine and drank from it.

'If you abuse her love, you will destroy all your hopes.'

Imitating Mary's voice Darnley said, ' "Oh what a fine king he will make, Davie." '

Controlling himself Riccio took Darnley's arm. 'Listen to me —'

'No,' said Darnley pulling away. '*Listen to her*, "I must have him, Davie." Oh she shall have me and I shall be master.'

He flourished a hand under Riccio's nose.

'Kiss the hand of your King, Davie, and I will forgive you. Come, kneel to me. Say: "I will love and serve you, King Henry".'

Riccio made no further attempt. He began to dress.

'Go to your room. It would not do for the future King of Scotland to be found here at this time of night. It is, you understand my lord, in God's hands only. But you are reckless to scorn your only friend.'

Momentarily Darnley was frightened by Riccio's change of tone, and his reply was partly an attempt to ingratiate himself.

'Now the sly little Italian will try poison against me. He will whisper in her ear. He will plant doubts. He fears to lose his place. He need not fear that. He will do very well under the new king. After all it is not in God's hands, Davie, it is in mine.'

Bothwell had chambers at the other end of Holyrood Palace. He woke at once when his page, Andrew, entered in the darkness and whispered, 'My lord.'

'What is it?'

'The Queen.'

'Fetch a light.'

Bothwell slept half-dressed. He got out of bed, put a cloak around his shoulders and came out of his bedroom into the main room of the apartment. Andrew was lighting candles. The Queen stood there, her face shadowed by the hood.

'Your grace?'

She glanced towards Andrew.

71

'Get out Andrew,' he said. 'And guard the door.'

When he was gone he said, 'Will you sit, your grace?'

'No.'

He regretted that he could see neither her features clearly, nor her hands which were hidden under the cloak, to judge her mood. Well, he thought, she'll spill it all out in a second. She's incapable of holding her tongue.

Mary said, 'The time has come for me to rule this land.'

CHAPTER SIX

The English ambassador to Scotland was suffering from indigestion. He was not a brave man. He disliked Scotland; feared the Scottish lords; longed to return to London where a man could live in a civilized fashion and breathe the spiced air at court. But he had his duty to do and he braced himself to do it. He wished he had not eaten his breakfast, however. Better by far to have that hollow, empty, dull feeling in the chest than this acid which seemed as if it would burn its way through to his spine.

The doors to Mary's presence chamber opened. He was aware of the French guards on either side of him and the Queen herself seated upon the throne under the canopy facing him. Not far from the Queen the object of the ambassador's audience, Henry Stuart, Lord Darnley, in a fine new green suit that the Queen had given him, lounged against the wall. Riccio was there and the priest Ballard, but there was no sign of James Stuart or any of the Lords of the Congregation.

The ambassador bowed and the acid stabbed him like a sword. He straightened up, coughed and said in a strangled voice, 'Your grace. I am required by my mistress, Elizabeth of England, to speak to Henry Stuart, Lord Darnley.'

'Do so. I am not his keeper as is Elizabeth of her lords, I'm told.'

The ambassador turned towards Darnley.

'My lord, you are ordered to England by your Queen.'

Darnley said, 'I like it well enough here,' and giggled.

'On your allegiance you are ordered, sir.'

'I acknowledge no duty or obedience save to this Queen,' said Darnley.

'Then,' said the ambassador grimly, 'you are a traitor.'

Mary rose. 'No,' she said, 'he is my loyal subject and I will protect him.'

Elizabeth had said to Cecil, 'Order Darnley home. Ignore protocol. That will provoke her and rouse her fine spirit in defiance. I want them married!'

Cecil was troubled. 'But, madam, she might agree, or James Stuart may force her to send him packing, believing it will please you.'

'Why then, Sir William, first we will treat him abominably and second we will let him escape back to the lady who will be pining for him no doubt. Have you no wits left or is it your age?'

'Neither, madam, it is that I alone among your council must at all times speak what I think are the dangers and risk your anger. I will send orders to the ambassador.'

Her mood changed. She took his arm. She said, 'William, you are my right arm.'

He smiled, which he seldom did, being a watchful and grossly overworked man.

'I will see that he speaks as sharply to her as you yourself would do.'

The English ambassador braced himself for it and said, 'I am instructed to tell you, madam, that you are merely a puppet queen. You play at ruling like a little girl with a dolls' house and you will not protect this traitor for I will speak to your brother the Lord James Stuart. It is he who has the wisdom here and can make good policy.'

And then he turned and strode from the presence chamber.

Mary was murderous with rage, but at the same time she was elated. The moment had come unexpectedly. She said to Riccio, 'Get Bothwell now. Tell him it is now. He must hurry.'

Then she composed herself and sat. A few moments later the door from the turret room to the presence chamber opened and Bothwell stood there.

'Madam?'

'Are you ready?'

'Yes.'

'Then make no mistake.'

'In these matters,' he said, 'I am an expert,' and closed the door.

Now, she thought, now.

Riccio, who remained in the presence chamber after fetching Bothwell by the secret back way, was frightened. He wiped the sweat off his face. He did not lack moral courage but physical violence terrified him.

James Stuart pushed open the doors to the presence chamber.

'Madam,' he said pointing at Darnley, 'we must not quarrel over so cheap a cause. I value the friendship of England. I fear this gentleman must leave us.'

'Brother,' said Mary, and her voice was steady, 'I order you to make all preparations for my marriage to Lord Darnley.'

Stuart, shaken, said, 'I forbid it. He is a Catholic and neither I nor John Knox will stomach another Papist ruler in this land.'

The anger which had been building in Mary since the English ambassador's words burst out.

'Knox, that hypocrite who in his lust has just married for the second time a mere girl of fifteen. That ageing lecher who hides behind the words of God?'

'Madam, you forget yourself.'

'No, by God, I do not. You shall not prevent my happiness.'

'I will speak to you again when you have control of yourself,' replied Stuart. 'And you, sir, pack and prepare to leave.'

He turned to go. Mary stood up and said, 'Guards.'

The two French men-at-arms dropped their pikes to bar the door from the presence chamber. Stuart at once drew his sword. Mary in triumph cried out, 'Bothwell!'

The door from the turret chamber burst open and Bothwell entered with six of his borderers. They ringed Stuart. Being a realist he lowered his sword. Bothwell sheathed his own sword and moving to Stuart took his from him.

'It was a bad day for you, Jamie,' he said cheerfully, 'when you betrayed me to the English and sold off my lands.'

Mary now came face to face with her brother.

'From this moment I alone will rule in Scotland,' she said. 'You have kept me caged, brother, but now who is caged?'

She turned to Riccio.

'Master Riccio!'

He came reluctantly to her side.

'David Riccio,' she said, 'from this moment you are my chief minister.'

Bothwell, taken by surprise, reacted sharply and began to protest but Mary went on, 'James Stuart, Earl of Moray, I banish you from my Kingdom. Give up your seals and keys of office.'

Stuart's composure broke for a moment.

'Riccio,' he said, 'you are a Catholic, be sure that you are confessed and in a state of grace each hour for from this moment I promise you death is at your shoulder.'

Before Riccio could reply Bothwell said fiercely, 'Madam, if you value your safety either imprison him or execute him.'

'I did not ask for your advice.'

'But you shall have it. When he has gone the other lords will bow the knee to you, then when he returns they will join him again for bloody revenge on all here.'

'I will not begin my reign like a tyrant.' Her anger was directed at him now. 'Escort my chief minister and see that all is in order. Then take James Stuart to the border. Return as soon as possible, there are preparations to be made for my marriage to Lord Darnley.'

They went. Mary turned to Darnley and stretched her hands out to him. He took them and they gazed at each other.

'My love,' said Mary.

'My love,' said Darnley and they kissed.

Ballard moved to leave the room. Mary became aware of him, laughed and said, 'Did you see, Father? Did you see?'

Ballard said coolly, 'I saw.'

'But for this gentleman,' went on Mary, 'who will be my husband, I would not have had the courage to act.'

'You do not lack courage, madam.'

She picked up his tone.

'You mean I lack other qualities? I see that no sooner have I banished one master than others hurry to give me advice and hedge me in. I will not submit again. I warn you I'll have my way. Will you marry us or must I find someone else?'

Ballard said, 'I will do it.'

All the bells of Edinburgh swung and pealed and pigeons exploded from the bell towers in white clouds. On the ramparts of Edinburgh Castle the gunners fired the saluting cannon as from the flag staff the royal standard of Scotland was broken out to flutter in the wind. To this background of joyful sound Mary and Darnley walked a carpet unrolled before them by servants. The French guards in new and splendid uniforms ran ahead to line the route. The crowd

76

which jammed the courtyard to the chapel royal pressed round the couple. When the guards tried to push them back with pike butts Mary stopped them. She was in a daze of happiness.

'No,' she said, 'No, these are my good and loving people.'

The people cheered and threw their bonnets in the air. Some were clownish and capered; some scraped on fiddles and some pushed close to touch the wedding gown and the bride's cloak. A woman brought her baby to be touched by Mary.

Mary said, 'It is my pleasure to walk among you on my wedding day. Rejoice with me in my happiness.'

They laughed and clapped and it was very different from the day she first came to Edinburgh. She walked ahead of Darnley and she shouted, 'Distribute the largesse. Give my good people gold.'

Her servants ran through the crowd, throwing handfuls of gold coins, and the good people scrabbled for it on hands and knees. One of them got in Darnley's path and Darnley kicked him out of the way. Not far behind him came the lords: Ruthven and Huntly and Morton, then in a group Argyll and Arran, Erskine and Gordon, Herries and Kirkcaldy of Grange, Lindsay and Mar. They had one quality in common – an infinite capacity for treachery. On this fine morning their interest lay in supporting the queen of Scotland who was in power. So when Darnley kicked a Scotsman from his path they laughed and applauded and Morton cried out, 'He will remember you, your grace.'

Darnley, already lost to all reason, shouted back, 'All the world will remember me, my lords, for I was born to be a king.'

Mary heard him and turned fondly towards him. From the chapel Riccio came to greet them, bowing and smiling and spreading his peacock feathers, and the lords noted it.

Inside the chapel royal, flowers were banked up from floor to ceiling. Mary and Darnley exchanged the marriage vows and three rings were placed on Mary's finger. Now it was done and only death could undo it.

The Queen's apartment, too, was full of flowers. When they were alone for the first time after the ceremony they embraced and began to kiss.

'My love,' she said, 'my dear love.'

'I love you more than my life,' said Darnley.

'I am so full of joy,' whispered Mary clinging to him. 'I am frightened even to speak of it.'

For a moment she was in terror that this great happiness would be taken from her, as Francis had been. There was a knock on the door.

'Enter,' she said, 'enter.'

Fleming came in. 'Madam.'

'What is it?'

'The Lord Bothwell wishes to see you.'

'Send him away,' said Darnley sharply.

'No,' said Mary at once. 'No, of course not. We owe him a great debt. Wait here for me. I will speak to him before we go out to the people.'

Bothwell was dressed for travel. He stood impatiently in the centre of the presence chamber.

'Now that you have chosen a King,' he said rapidly, 'it is time that I left the court to care for my affairs.'

She was taken aback and said, 'I need you here, Bothwell.'

'But, my lady,' he replied, 'you now have a husband to protect you.'

He could not keep the edge out of his voice.

'He will lead your army, put down such of your lords as intrigue against you and make wise policy, I have no doubt.'

His tone was so scathing that even Mary in her day of happiness could not fail to understand him. She said at once, 'Do you oppose my marriage? Is that it?'

'I never oppose the rightful monarch. I have grown poor in the habit.'

'I will not be mocked.'

'Mocked?' he said. 'I could not find words to mock a Queen of Scotland who chooses a smooth-faced boy as her master, and a baseborn Italian as her chief minister.'

'Go then,' flared Mary. 'Leave the court and stay from it.'

He strode to the door.

'Bothwell.'

He stopped.

'You have grown poor in my service, you say?'

'I have.'

'Very well,' said Mary offensively, 'you shall be paid off, my good lord.'

'I can manage well enough without.'

'Spare me your arrogance. I will give you money.'

'Save it,' said Bothwell, 'to buy suits for your husband.'

She knew he was thinking of the wedding gifts, violet velvet for a dressing-gown, cloth of gold for the caparison of his horse, bonnets with feathers . . . She thought, that's why he's angry. He believes himself displaced.

'You are jealous of the King,' she said. 'You think I will value you less.'

Bothwell chose his words with care. 'You could say, your Majesty, with truth that I am jealous.'

There had been a moment, on the night she visited him to plan the overthrow of Stuart, when the light from the candles caught her face and hair and he suddenly thought, you are a real woman, unawakened I'll swear, but a real woman and you have courage. From that moment he wanted her.

Mary was saying, 'Then you are foolish.'

For she took his meaning to be political and that it was a form of apology. This was a day above all days to be generous.

'With Harry to support and comfort me, with Riccio to advise me and with you, Bothwell, to keep order in the realm it will be a golden time. Soon we will march South into England. It will be a holy crusade. I am the hope of my

English Catholic subjects and at last I will restore their Church to them. I will destroy Elizabeth who has tyrannized over them and then by God's grace I will rule my two kingdoms as I was ordained to do. That is my dream. Will you stay at court and share it with me?'

Bothwell was silent. Mary put out a hand to him. She said gently, 'My lord.'

He appeared to relent and took her hand and kissed it.

'I will return,' he said, 'when I have settled my affairs on the border.'

Once more he strode away to the door.

'How soon?'

'When I have married for money.'

He shut the door firmly behind him.

Mary was again completely taken aback. She had never considered, from the moment that they first met, that he would have anything else in life to do but serve her.

'Marry?' she said, unaccountably upset. 'Not without the permission of your Queen, my good lord, I promise you that.'

The Queen's great bed was made of woods of many different colours and it had a choice of quilts, some silk, some velvet, some gold, some silver and some of embroidery. The curtains which could be pulled between the four posts to keep out the cold were as various as the quilts and made to match them. Over the whole was a canopy. On this night the curtains were drawn.

They lay naked, close together. Elizabeth like a cat licked his ear and said, 'How well that lady in Scotland took the bait. We shall see no more foreign princes or foreign armies in Scotland.'

She stroked his beard, twining her fingers in it.

'Did you really believe I would ever let you go, Robin?'

Dudley said drily, 'Yes, I did believe it.'

'And that I would give her my throne in writing? My whole kingdom?'

'That,' he said, 'was harder to believe, I confess.'

She began to pinch him so that he was forced to pinion her hands and put one leg across her to hold her down. She was laughing.

'Not even in the moment of my death,' she said, 'would I name her my successor.'

He was glad the darkness hid his face. His lust for power was very great, and he had been sure when he rode North to Scotland that eventually he would be the king of both Scotland and England.

'I have always hated Darnley's family,' said Elizabeth. 'When my sister was alive and I a prisoner, existing daily between life and death, his mother was the one lady at court who mocked me. There was a time when I was ill and without friends and she was my keeper. She installed the cooks and the serving men in the apartment above mine and day and night the sound went on so that I never slept and thought I would die. And his father is the most evil of men.'

'Why?' said Dudley, surprised.

'In my father's wars with Scotland, Darnley's father took children as hostages for the good conduct of Scottish horsemen in his ranks. When they deserted he hanged the children and their ghosts haunt him.'

Dudley shivered. 'Is it true?'

'It is true.'

Dudley said suddenly, 'Now I understand. For three nights when Darnley first came to the court of Mary ghostly warriors fought in the streets of Edinburgh. No one could see them, but the sound of battle raged till the small hours of the morning. It was an omen.'

'Yes,' said Elizabeth, 'it was an omen. He will destroy her.'

He was drunk. He suddenly shouted, 'I am the King.'

She was appalled.

In the presence chamber, heads were turning towards the door of the turret room and the music faltered. His shouting voice was heard again, 'I will be obeyed.'

More dancers stopped and the music tailed off. The door from the turret room burst open and Darnley stood there swaying. Riccio, on the far side of the presence chamber, alert for danger, caught the eye of Andrew who was passing and whispered, 'What has happened?'

Darnley in the background shouted, 'I am the King.'

Gradually from front to back of the whole chamber all the lords bowed, and the servants and the musicians. The ladies dropped into deep curtsies. Andrew, who had just left the turret chamber, whispered, 'He is angry with the Queen, sir. She would not obey him and return my master's wedding gift.'

Darnley hurled the glass which he had been holding to smash on the floor in the space between himself and the nearest lords. He looked at the bowed heads in front of him. He had a new idea.

'On the night of his marriage a King shall be served by his lords.'

He pointed as he named them. 'Douglas, Falconside, Ruthven, Morton, you shall serve me. Come. We will show the Queen who is the master.'

Those named did not move. Darnley stumbled, recovered himself, put his hand on the hilt of his dagger and began to move to the nearest, who was Morton. He was drunk enough to try it.

Riccio reacted bravely. Moving fast and speaking at the same time he placed himself deliberately between Darnley and the lords. He made himself the target and he knew well how much they hated him.

He said in a loud voice, 'Your grace, I am the chief minister. I will serve you. I will kneel to serve you if you wish but let these good lords continue their pleasure on this happy night.'

Darnley raised his arms as if to smash Riccio. Riccio braced himself to be struck and to bear the ignominy of it. Some of the lords laughed out loud with approval and Darnley hearing this realized how he could use their hatred. At the last moment instead of striking Riccio he put an arm round his shoulders.

'No, no,' he said. 'They shall serve us both, Davie. I order it.'

Holding the small Italian tightly by the shoulders and forcing him round to face the company he shouted, 'But for this good and loving friend I would not be the King. He too shall be served.'

Riccio was horrified. Throughout the whole assembly there was an ugly murmur of dissent and hatred. He dared not look at the murderous faces. He knew that the whims of the Queen's husband must be tolerated as long as that Queen reigned, but the deadly insult offered to the lords when they were made to serve him would never be forgiven.

Trying to make Darnley remember their love for each other he pleaded, 'No, no, your Majesty. I beg you to excuse me.'

Darnley relished the fear in Riccio's voice. It restored his humour.

'I order you to sit with me,' he said lovingly. 'This is your reward, chief minister, for speaking to the Queen for your friend.'

In the turret room Mary heard Darnley's voice, 'The food is cooling, my lords. Come now and show your obedience.'

The door was pushed wide open. Darnley, still with a hand on Riccio's shoulder, entered the chamber and shouted at the servants in the background, 'Get out, get out, we have better servants here.'

They tried to hurry away but found it difficult to get

through the door because the lords were entering. They flattened themselves against the wall but did not escape being struck by the lords forcing their way into the narrow room.

Darnley bowed contemptuously to Mary and then propelled Riccio to the table. Mary sat.

Darnley said, 'Sit by the Queen. It is your right for you are a king-maker.'

As Riccio sat the lords Falconside, Ruthven, Morton and Douglas bowed, each in turn, formally to Mary and moved to begin to serve.

Darnley said, 'See how I am obeyed, madam.'

And Mary, white with anger said icily, 'I see how you will behave if ever you are granted the crown matrimonial and become King in your own right, my lord.'

Morton began to pour wine for Mary, and Darnley, drunkenly failing to understand her meaning, said thickly, 'They obey me.'

He looked up at Morton.

'When the Queen is served, serve the chief minister. Serve him before me. Serve the little Italian.'

He patted Riccio on the cheek.

'He is the Pope's friend.'

Riccio glanced desperately at Mary. Morton, who was pouring, hesitated fractionally. Darnley leant close to Riccio and smiled at him. For one terrible moment Riccio thought that Darnley would kiss him full on the lips there in front of the Queen. Instead Darnley said, 'Now their hatred for you will be so great, Davie, there will be none left for me.'

He raised his voice as the lords approached with the food. 'Take my napkin, good minister, to keep the stains from your rich clothes.'

Then he rose, glass in hand, and said, 'My lords, I drink a toast to my firstborn.'

He drank the glass to the dregs and hurled it to shatter against the wall.

*   *   *

Just before dawn, at the time when the worst dreams come, Mary stood by the window of the bedchamber wrapped in a gown, her hair hanging over her shoulders, and looked towards her bridal bed. Darnley lay there naked, sprawled on his face. The bed itself looked as if it had been torn half to pieces. He was snoring intermittently. His mouth was open and he dribbled. His lovemaking had been so brutal and so inept that Mary was still shocked and in pain for she had been a virgin before he began. In the few hours that stretched between the marriage and its consummation her world was broken. She went over in her mind every moment since her first meeting with Darnley when the great passion of the flesh had seized her, so that she was blinded to every quality except his physical beauty. She forced herself to look at him and see him as she now knew him to be.

She said out loud, 'I loathe you.'

CHAPTER SEVEN

Mary on a white horse, a hawk upon her wrist, lifted her face to the clear sky and revelled in a sense of freedom such as she had not had for many months. She had made her decision on the preceding day. The hunting attendants, and her servants, who had suffered with her through the past months, also seemed as if a load had been lifted from them. They were laughing and chattering to each other in French. Even Mary Seton, who disliked riding, seemed to be enjoying the morning.

Then they heard someone shouting in the distance. They saw a horseman riding hell for leather, using whip and spur, towards them. Seton anxiously rode to Mary's side. Mary, too, had recognized him and said, 'Draw the others away, Seton. Do so now.'

'But, your grace —'

'Draw the others away, Seton, and do it cheerfully.'

Seton called out, 'Ride on, the Queen will follow.'

They cantered away leaving Mary to face Darnley. He was bellowing at her before he got to her.

'You must return at once.'

When he reined up she said, 'Are you drunk as ever?'

He tried to placate her because he was frightened.

'No, no, forgive me, Mary, but there is a plot and you must return.'

Mary looked at the heaving and bloody flanks of his horse and the foam round its mouth.

'Will you ride the poor beast to death?'

She remembered Francis in agony pulling hard on a jaw-breaker bit and putting his spurs to a horse and riding out to die. She said quietly, 'Perhaps you, too, are ill.'

Darnley paid no attention. He was saying, 'I beg you to listen to me. Something has happened that threatens us.'

'Are you ill?' asked Mary. 'Is that why you are drunken and vicious and stupid? Is it your fate to look like a god and yet have in you so rotten and debauched a spirit that you cannot help yourself? I would like to believe that for then I could forgive you the bitter shame and despair you have caused me these past months.'

Darnley was opening and shutting his mouth like a fool trying to interrupt her.

He shouted desperately, 'Think what you like but come back with me at once; there is a plot. We shall lose all if we hesitate. Your own guards turned me back from the royal apartments. When I drew my dagger on them they threatened to kill me. To kill a King.'

It's no use she thought, there is nothing to be done with him. She said bitingly, 'You are not the King, you are the king consort – that is all. You are called King Henry for form's sake only, and that in deference to me. You are merely Henry, Lord Darnley, who married a Queen, and if that Queen dies you will be Henry, Lord Darnley again and have no rights in this land – and I tell you, *you shall have none* for I will never grant you the crown matrimonial.'

Then he realized. 'It was you who ordered the guards to keep me out.'

'Yes.'

'You have shamed me. The whole court will gibe at me.'

'Then leave the court.'

'And I am forbidden your bed?'

'You shall never come near me again. I will not suffer it.'

To Darnley only one explanation was possible. He said at once, 'You love another.'

Mary said contemptuously, 'Ride home, my lord. Arrange your new apartments. I ordered that they should be suitable to your rank and station.'

She turned her horse and rode after the rest of her party. Darnley shouted, 'I will be revenged.'

Seton, who had hung back from the others, heard him.

'Madam, I fear for you.'

Darnley shouted again, 'I will be revenged.'

Mary said sadly, 'He is already revenged.'

'Madam?'

'I am with child It is the third month.'

The pregnancy of queens and the degeneracy of kings does not reduce the necessary business of State from day to day. Mary continued to work with Riccio. She slept badly and found it easier to work by night rather than lie awake regretting her folly over Darnley and dreading the birth of the child which he had fathered on her.

So it was past midnight when the doors to Riccio's apartment burst open. Darnley stood there swaying and drunk. His clothes were stained. She had not seen him for so long she was surprised that he had a small beard. They were close to each other when he entered, confirming his suspicion. The curve of Mary's pregnancy could be clearly seen under her gown and Darnley stood looking at it for a moment.

'What do you want?' she said 'Why do you break in so wildly? Are you ill?'

'I know who is the King here,' he said 'And I know who will bear his bastard. I know why you come creeping here at night to keep him secret company in his chamber.'

Mary was aghast and she cried out, 'The child is yours, God help me.'

'I will be revenged on you, I promise you.'

He had a dagger at his waist. Although he did not touch it Riccio stepped in front of Mary and said quietly, 'I am your enemy. I have spoken against you when I can. You are not fit to rule. But the child is yours.'

Darnley began to weep with self-pity. 'You have destroyed me. You have destroyed me.'

He said to Mary, 'I disgust you. You loved me and now I disgust you. I am lost. I am lost.'

He stumbled from the room.

Mary was trembling. 'He is certainly mad. I must act against him.'

'No.'

'But next time he may try to kill me.'

'You must do nothing until the child is born. No shadow, doubt, stain or scandal must touch the child. You carry in you a monarch who will inherit two kingdoms to the glory of God and in the name of the holy Catholic Church.'

She leaned on the desk with both hands and slowly the trembling subsided.

'You are right,' she said. 'I am ashamed of my weakness.'

She was near to fainting. She sat in the chair by the desk and Riccio brought wine to her. He was worried to see how pale she was; she seemed to have lost that wonderful and generous spirit which so captivated all who came in touch with her.

'It must be God's will,' she said sadly, 'that I live through such a bitter time. I will pray to bear it.'

In a corner of the passage-way which led to his room Darnley leant against a wall and was sick. Then he turned and began to grope his way towards his door. He stumbled and fell on one knee. From an archway two figures seized him and, before he could cry out, put a gag in his mouth and hurried him along the corridor and down steps and round corners until he lost all sense of direction.

A door slammed behind him. The gag was taken from his mouth. In a low, vaulted chamber stood all the Lords of the Congregation. This grim phalanx, silent and still, lit by torches which flamed and smoked in brackets on the wall, struck terror into Darnley. He sank speechless to his knees. In front of the lords was a small table and on it a document. Ruthven spoke first in his gasping voice.

'Stand up, your Majesty.'

'Don't kill me. Don't kill me.'

'We are your loyal subjects.'

The two who had brought him hauled him to his feet and supported him until it seemed that he could stand on his own; then they joined their fellows. Huntly said encouragingly, 'We believe that you are much wronged, your grace.'

The first cautious hope rose in him. Ruthven croaked, 'You are both wronged and shamed.'

'By God, I am. The Papal spy, Riccio, has bewitched the Queen.'

'True. True,' said several voices.

'It is an unnatural thing for a woman to rule,' said Falconside.

'And it is most unnatural,' growled Morton, 'that all the great lords of Scotland sit in council like naughty boys at school to be lorded over by the little Papist when there is a true King in the land.'

The terror struck Darnley again. This was a cruel game, a prelude to much worse things. It was to be their revenge for the wedding night.

'You mock me,' he said almost crying. 'I am not the King. I am the king consort, which is to say a puppet king, shut off from all power. You know this. Why do you mock me?'

'We,' said Ruthven, 'your loyal subjects, will make you the true King.'

'We the council,' said Morton, 'will grant you the crown matrimonial to rule here. To be first in the land.'

And Falconside said, 'If this is done, your grace, *you will rule even if the Queen is dead.*'

His head ached and the stink of the torches almost made him sick again. He wiped the back of his hand across his mouth and tried to swallow the stale taste of vomit. Was it possible? Was his revenge at hand? Morton suddenly raised a clenched fist and shouted; the noise in the confined space after the quiet intensity of the preceding voices was appalling and he shrank from it.

Morton shouted, 'King Henry I of Scotland and the Isles!'

And they all roared, 'Long live the King!'

Darnley looked cunningly from one face to another.

'What must I do to gain the prize?'

Morton said, 'Embrace the Protestant faith and defend it against all Papists in the land.'

'The Queen is a Papist,' said Darnley.

'All Papists.'

'With all my heart,' exclaimed Darnley.

Ruthven held up the document. 'We have drawn up this covenant. On our part we pledge you the crown, and that we will pursue, slay and extirpate all who oppose this resolution.'

For the first time in many months Darnley laughed aloud. He was very happy.

'You will cut Davie's throat.'

'There is no word of killing in the bond.'

'And if need be,' said Darnley deliberately, 'you will kill one other.'

'We have all signed the bond,' replied Morton ambiguously.

There was an impressive array of seals and signatures on it. Darnley was now enjoying himself.

'Then no man among you,' he said, looking at it, 'will dare betray another. This form of covenant is a good Scottish custom.'

They looked bleakly back at him.

Ruthven said harshly, 'It lacks one signature.'

Morton offered him a quill. 'On your part you will hold us innocent and defend us *even in the presence of the Queen herself* no matter what action we have to take to make you king.'

'Is that all?' said Darnley.

Falconside said, 'You will pardon and recall James Stuart, Earl of Moray.'

'Agreed.'

But he did not take the quill.

'Then sign, your Majesty,' said Ruthven, 'and hasten the great day of your coronation.'

'I have one further condition.'

'Name it.'

Darnley took a deep breath, then he said, 'That you will kill him in her presence when I am there to see the deed.'

He paused, then he said, 'And she must come to no harm *before* that moment.'

Morton dipped the quill in the ink and offered to him. He took it and wrote an extra clause at the bottom of the document, before signing it.

*   *   *

Three weeks later Elizabeth of England held in her hand a copy of the murder bond. It included the clause written by Darnley. She was in the council chamber with Cecil and Dudley. She was incredulous.

'Is it true?' she said.

'Our good ambassador,' replied Cecil, 'has vouched for it and everyone in the Scottish court knows of it, save the Queen and the Italian.'

'And her loving husband has put his signature and seal to it,' said Elizabeth, 'in the original that is – can we be sure of that?'

'Yes,' said Cecil. 'He has signed.'

'So much for marriage,' said Elizabeth.

Inwardly Cecil groaned. He knew his fate should Elizabeth die unmarried and childless. Now that Mary was pregnant the danger was acute for half England would welcome her with open arms.

Elizabeth had turned her back on him. She no longer wanted a part in the events which she had set in train when Darnley rode North.

Cecil said, 'Madam, the Lord James Stuart is ready to travel to Scotland.'

'So?'

'He must have money. To hold the lords he must pay the lords.'

'Let him find it elsewhere.'

'But everything has happened as you hoped,' protested Cecil, 'and now we must support our Protestant friends. This is our moment.'

Elizabeth turned on him. 'That is a murder bond,' she shouted. 'Drawn up by treacherous subjects against their Queen. Where is my name on it? Where does it say that Elizabeth of England shall pay the wages of the assassins?'

Cecil remembered his lost fifty pounds and said, 'It was you who sent Darnley to her.'

'Yes,' replied Elizabeth, 'but the rest is in God's hands and I leave this to Him also. Come, Robin.'

If Dudley had kept his mouth shut and taken her from the gloomy council chamber and out onto the river he might well have got his own way that day but instead he said, thinking it would further his own cause, 'Do not forget, Madam, that the lady is with child.'

Elizabeth's true feelings burst out. 'Dear God. How long must I live in the shadow of this other Queen? I wish her without power but not dead. Her death threatens me. I fear her death. She is an anointed Queen as I am. By God, if it were not for policy I have it in me to ride North into her very palace and warn her of what is to come.'

'Madam,' said Cecil gently and he held up the document, 'these gentlemen are set upon a certain course. It is as wise for us as for them that they pursue it to the end.'

'Then let them,' said Elizabeth, 'find the means.'

'Sweet Majesty,' said Dudley completing his act of folly, 'if you would but marry and bear a child yourself then her shadow would be lifted from you.'

That did it. Elizabeth said at once to Cecil, 'Master Cecil, pay three thousand pounds in gold to the Earl of Moray and send him home on a fast horse.'

Cecil smiled.

'And let the gold coin,' she said, 'be of any kind save that which has my head on it for I will have no knowledge of her death. See to it.'

She left the council chamber with Dudley unhappily in tow. Cecil knelt and put his hands together and modestly bowed his head.

'Almighty God,' he said, 'I thank Thee for the endless ambition of the Earl of Leicester to be king and for the many times it has provoked the Queen's Majesty to wise policy against her will but to Thy glory, Amen.'

Under cover of night they converged upon the Palace at

Holyrood. When the first of them entered the courtyard below the turret room the French sentry on duty was not alarmed for he recognized the lord. Morton strode up to him and said in broad Scots, 'I hope you've said your prayers'. And put a knife in his throat and caught him as he fell.

The others crowded into the courtyard; many wore armour. Last came Darnley, a jackal among wolves. He took his dagger from its sheath and handed it to Morton.

The soft light of wax candles in silver candelabra lighted the supper party. Riccio wore a fine coat trimmed with damask and fur. He felt the Scottish cold despite the cheerful fire behind him. They were laughing as he told a scurrilous story about Elizabeth.

'... and then she was so demanding,' he said, 'of his affections that the poor man dare not be reconciled with his own wedded wife for fear of the royal anger.'

They were still laughing when the tapestry in the doorway of the bedroom was lifted to one side. Ruthven stood there. He was dressed in black armour – and now, in the last stages of consumption, burning with fever, his face white and his breath gasping, he was like the figure of death. Seton cried out with shock and Riccio was struck with terror as he turned and saw him.

Mary said at once, 'Why are you here?'

'Let it please your Majesty that David Riccio come out of this privy chamber where he has hidden too long.'

'It is by my command,' said Mary, 'that he is here.'

'He has offended your honour.'

'You have a fever,' said Mary, 'and your mind is full of fantasy.'

She turned to the servants. 'Escort this lord away and lock the doors.'

Hesitantly the servants attempted to obey her. Ruthven drew his sword and said, 'Lay not hands on me.'

At his shout the door from the presence chamber was

flung-open and there were the fierce and murderous lords. They rushed into the turret room. Riccio, in a panic, ran to Mary and grovelled behind her clinging to her skirts. The press of the lords forcing their way into the room overturned the dining-table. Plates, knives, dishes, glasses went smashing to the floor. The candelabra fell and all the candles were snuffed except one which Seton caught as it slid from the table. She held it up and it was by this light and the reflection from the fire that Mary saw what followed. The brighter light in the bedroom and the presence chamber showed the two doorways filled with the dark and terrible silhouettes of the lords.

Riccio screamed out to her, 'Save me, save me. In the name of God, I beg you to save me.'

Guided by his voice Darnley forced his way to him. He bent and seized one of Riccio's hands in both of his own. He pulled it clear of Mary's skirt and tried to drag Riccio where the lords could get at him. He was not strong enough. Another lord seized the wrist of the hand which Darnley was holding. Darnley at once got hold of the fingers of Riccio's other hand which was still clinging to Mary's skirt and bent one of them back until it broke. Riccio screamed and let go and was dragged away towards the bedchamber.

At that moment Falconside stepped over the debris and the table and placed a pistol to Mary's swollen belly. Seeing this clearly, in the candlelight, Seton screamed. Mary, who had been trying to follow Riccio to save him, became aware of the pistol and stood quite still, accepting her own death in that moment. She tried to pray. Falconside pressed the trigger. The pistol did not fire. In the frenzy of the preceding moments he had forgotten to cock it. Realizing this he at once began to wrench the cocking handle. Darnley, half frantic with excitement and fear, involuntarily pushed the pistol to one side. He pointed towards Riccio being dragged through into the bedroom.

'Kill him!' he shouted. 'Kill him first.'

Riccio, who was near the bed, got an arm round one of the posts and pulling himself into a half-sitting position cried out despairingly, 'Harry, stop them. Harry!'

In the turret chamber Darnley gripped Mary, pushed her brutally against the wall and pinned her there. In the bedroom they kicked Riccio to move him on. One of them, more impatient than the others, prodded him with a dagger, not meaning to kill him. Despite their promise to Darnley it was not considered proper to finish off the base Italian in the royal apartments. He was to be slaughtered outside where the blood would not stain the expensive furnishings and tapestries. But this jab of the dagger, the spurt of blood after it and the high scream from Riccio woke the blood lust in them. They pressed in to stab him. They lunged and cut and slashed, and pushed each other out of the way to get at him. They cut each other in their frenzy. Riccio tried to pull himself to his feet. He seized the bed hangings and they tore down under his weight. Blood flowed out from him in half a dozen places, and he lurched out of the bedroom and into the presence chamber. He tripped headlong over the body of the dead French guard. The noise was tremendous as the noble lords and lairds bayed after his blood.

Riccio, screaming and lurching and scrabbling on his knees, moved about the presence chamber with the lords hunting him down. He died in the centre of the chamber of sixty wounds and the last was given by Morton, who stepped in close and said, 'This is from the King,' and drove Darnley's dagger into Riccio's throat up to the hilt. The howling stopped. The lords with bloody daggers in their hands stood round the small corpse to get their breath. They wiped their blades on the fine coat, and then they picked him up and began to pass him overhead from hand to hand. From the open window over the courtyard the body came spinning down to smash on the cobbles. Andrew, on horseback, reined briefly to look at it and then was off at the gallop.

The noise from the turret followed him for a mile through the night.

Ballard came down into the courtyard, ran to Riccio and knelt beside him. He prayed. Then he picked him up in his arms and carried him away. In the turret chamber Darnley released Mary. The terrified servants worked like madmen to clear the floor of the trampled mess of food and wine and broken glass and dishes. They righted and cleaned the table and chairs and re-lit the candles. In the bedroom Fleming and Seton on the edge of hysteria as their feet slipped on blood, cleared the torn and ripped bed hangings. The murder done, most of the lords left the apartment to secure the Palace against attack, or any attempt to rescue the Queen's person.

The squat Morton, Falconside whose pistol had misfired, and Ruthven came into the turret chamber. Ruthven, burning with fever, sat heavily at the table and called for wine. One of the servants instantly brought it to him and he drank and called for more. Mary could not control her shaking body and it was all she could do to force the words out, but she said to Darnley, 'You traitor and Judas.'

Ruthven gasped, trying to placate her, 'Speak gently to his Majesty.'

'Coward,' said Mary. 'Assassin.'

'Be silent,' said Morton.

'You shall all die for this.'

'Madam,' said Ruthven, 'speak more wisely. You are a prisoner.'

Mary turned to Darnley.

'Let the King say if I am a prisoner of his loyal subjects.'

The horrible spectacle of the nobility of Scotland in action had so unnerved Darnley that he could not stand up. He slumped opposite Ruthven, unable to face either Mary or the lords.

He muttered, 'We have saved you from great shame – from a sorcerer.'

'I will never rest,' replied Mary, 'until you have a sorer heart than I have now.'

'Papist filth,' shouted Falconside. 'He is dead and you will be silent.'

Mary shouted back, 'I have that in my belly which will be revenged on you all.'

'If you live,' roared Morton.

Ruthven gasped angrily, 'My lord do not threaten the heir to Scotland. He shall be born but we will keep this Queen *imprisoned* from that time.'

Mary was stunned.

'Imprisoned from that time?' she repeated.

'This good King,' sneered Morton, 'shall have the whole government of the realm. The heir we will bring up to the Protestant faith and you shall be a perpetual prisoner.'

She did not have to think what to do. It happened in her so strongly that she almost felt the pain which she pretended suddenly gripped her. She began to crumple to one side. She cried out and fell to her knees and Seton ran from the bedroom to support her. She clung to Seton and she gasped.

'The child. I believe it is the child. Help me. Help me.'

And then, quite deliberately, she put out a hand towards Darnley her husband whom she hated and said, 'Husband, help me. I believe our child may be born.'

Darnley rose guiltily to move away from her. Seton turned to the servants and rapped, 'Carry the Queen to her bed. Take her up gently.'

They hurried to obey her.

'Gently now,' said Seton. 'With all care and place the covers over her.'

The servants carried Mary into the bedchamber and in the doorway Seton made a deep curtsy to the lords.

She said humbly, 'My lords, I ask you to be merciful and give us privacy. If the Queen is in labour after these dreadful events then there must be calm or the child may die.'

'So be it,' said Ruthven.

Seton dropped the tapestry. Ruthven rose to go.

Darnley blurted out, 'I will stay.'

Morton looked hard at him and said, 'The Palace is guarded. You have chosen your way, your Majesty, and now you must tread it to the end.'

The warning in his voice was clear.

'I have chosen,' said Darnley. They closed the door on him. Darnley sat by the fire; his hands were shaking and suddenly he started to weep.

'Oh, Davie,' he wept. 'Davie. Poor Davie.'

In the bedroom Seton eased the tapestry at the doorway to make a small crack to spy on Darnley. Satisfied that he was settled she moved swiftly to the other door which gave into the presence chamber and this too she eased open a crack. On the far side one of the lords stood guard. She closed the door. Mary stood close to the bed ready to lie on it and continue the pretence. Seton came very close to her and whispered, 'The King is in there alone but the outer door is guarded.'

Mary said softly, 'They have forgotten the secret way if they ever knew it. Thank God, brother James is not here to remind them.'

She crossed to open it. She said, 'Take down my hair while I tell you what must be done.'

Seton began to unpin Mary's hair.

Mary said urgently to Fleming, 'Go to poor Davie's apartment. Find there my silver casket for it has many papers of State in it.'

As Fleming was making her way down the spiral staircase Mary said to Seton, 'We must get away tonight or we are lost. And we must take the King with us or they will find a way to give him the Crown and totally destroy my rights.'

'But how, madam, how?'

'Find Andrew If he has gone it will mean that he has fled to Bothwell. If not send him. Bothwell must come with horses for our escape. Then find Father Ballard and tell him to wait in the burial vaults for us. That will be our point of escape.'

Mary's hair was free and she spread it to fall wide over her shoulders.

'For my part,' she said, 'I will do what I must to make that traitor, my husband, into a double traitor.'

Seton hesitated to step into the darkness beyond the panel and descend the spiral staircase. Mary suddenly embraced her 'Be brave,' she said, 'God will watch over you.'

Seton kissed her hand and went. Mary closed the panel. For a moment she prepared herself then she walked firmly into the turret chamber where Darnley was sitting, tears upon his cheeks. She knelt. She took his nearest hand in both of hers and kissed it. She laid it to her cheek and when she looked up at him there were already tears on her face.

'Forgive me, Harry,' she whispered. 'Please forgive me.'

He pulled his hand away. 'What has become of your pain? Why are you here?'

'The child is alive within me. It is not yet time. I beg you to forgive my blindness. I have done you a great wrong. I must try to make amends.'

'It is too late,' exclaimed Darnley 'It is too late.'

Mary took his hand again.

'No I swear it is not. You shall be the king without the stain of being elected by murderers.'

'I have no choice,' he was weeping again. 'All the world will know tomorrow.'

Mary stroked his cheek. 'It was God's will,' she said. 'Davie was good and loyal but you could not let a usurper and commoner prevent your destiny.'

'That is true,' he said. 'That is true.'

Her extraordinary instinct and courage in the moment of greatest danger had shown her the way to deal with him. She behaved to him as if he were that poor, sad young Francis her first husband. And because he was maudlin drunk, and full of fear and self-pity, he succumbed to her gentle and soothing manner.

'My eyes have been opened,' she said, 'and I am utterly cast down by my folly. It is my fault. I was not loving enough. I did not understand you but even now it is not too late. All my fears now are for you, Harry. I am in terror that those same murderers will butcher you when they have your heir safe in their keeping.'

Darnley shook his head.

'They dare not.'

'They'd dare anything and they are cunning Think what has already happened. First they killed Davie as if for your sake. But they hate you as much as they did him. Now they have me prisoner until the child is born. Then with a helpless baby as the symbol of the monarch they can do what they yearn to do – rule everything here and live on English gold. And' – she shivered as if she were very frightened of what she had to say next – 'and, dear husband, they will bring James home.'

Frightened, Darnley said, 'It's true. He is coming. I had to summon him.'

'When he is here,' said Mary, 'and the heir is born, what will they do with King Henry?'

Darnley blurted out, 'There is a bond.'

At that moment Mary almost betrayed herself. With a great effort of will she kept the hatred out of her voice and said softly, 'You signed a bond with them?'

'Yes,' said Darnley. 'Yes. So I'm safe.'

'And you have it, of course,' she said.

'Why no,' said Darnley. 'Morton said that for safekeeping and my good name it must be hidden . . .'

He tailed off as he realized.

'They will kill you,' said Mary softly, 'and burn the bond.'

'What can I do? What can I do?' he said in despair.

She put her arms round him and deliberately began to kiss and caress him.

'Don't be afraid, Harry,' she said, 'I know what to do. Trust me. I am your loving wife. All you need do is trust me.'

And she kissed and soothed him until he began to respond. Not like a lover but like a frightened child.

'Tell me. Tell me. Tell me.'

In the burial chamber, the bones and skulls of the ancient kings of Scotland lay among broken sepulchres. Mary led Darnley by the hand on the hazardous journey through the Palace of Holyrood down to the dim and musty chamber. How long ago it seemed when she and another played truant, and ran hand in hand into the morning light. Now, hand in hand with the whimpering Darnley, she felt she had been shut up in a prison, or a tomb, for all her time in Scotland; that it was her destiny to be the centre of so many dark affairs that she would never see the face of the sun again.

Dust of the long dead lifted under their feet as they entered the vault. Darnley cried out in terror at the two figures, so still and ominous in the faint light. Ballard ignored him and spoke to Mary.

'The Lord Bothwell is waiting. I will lead you. Can you ride, your grace?'

He was anxious in case she should miscarry the child. Mary said firmly, 'I can ride – have you the casket, Seton.'

Seton held it up.

Bothwell waited beyond the high wall of the graveyard. The moon was up and bright overhead, and as they hurried towards the wicket gate Mary stumbled and fell over a newly turned grave.

Ballard, helping her to rise said, 'There lies David. I buried him.'

Mary knelt again.

Andrew appeared at the wicket gate motioning them to hurry.

'Hurry,' said Darnley, 'Hurry, for God's sake.'

'Go on,' said Mary.

Darnley immediately ran.

'Poor Davie,' said Mary. 'Good and faithful servant, may God have mercy on your soul.'

Bothwell and two of his followers each led a spare horse. Darnley was running towards them when Seton came through the gate. He immediately mounted one of the horses. When Mary appeared she cried out, 'My lord, wait. I cannot run for fear I miscarry.'

Darnley shouted back, 'Miscarry if you will. We can make another when we are safe,' and kicked his horse to a gallop. Bothwell was out of the saddle and running to Mary. He said very cheerfully when he got to her, 'It seems a little dagger work brings out the best in you, your grace.'

Mary was panting and outraged by Darnley.

'But not in you,' she said furiously. 'We are one horse short I see.'

And they were.

'I will stay behind,' said Ballard.

'You will ride,' snapped Mary. 'I order you. Mount and ride.'

Ballard obeyed and by now the borderers had Seton in the saddle of the third horse.

'Then you, my gracious lady,' said Bothwell, 'must pluck up your skirts and ride with me for if we are caught here they will cut us to collops and feed us to the dogs.'

He helped her up and mounted behind her. As he was doing this he laughed and said, 'We must bless the darkness of the night for it most modestly veils the legs of the Queen.'

He put his arms round her to hold the reins.

'If this horse had a name it would go down in history, but as I stole it some hours ago in Edinburgh it will not be remembered. Are you comfortable, madam?'

Mary was smiling in the darkness. 'Ride on,' she said.

*　　　　*　　　　*

Stuart rode out of Berwick and over the border on the night of the murder as arranged. He arrived at Holyrood the following day. They took him up to the royal apartments. The doors into the turret room and the royal bedroom from the presence chamber were smashed and hung from their hinges. The lords who had signed the murder bond were all gathered in the presence chamber. He said nothing as he moved through them and into the bedchamber. The secret panel in the wall still stood open.

Stuart said almost sadly, 'Like others before you, my lords, you have underestimated a Stuart and now we shall have civil war in this land.'

CHAPTER EIGHT

It was late afternoon as they came over the skyline of wild Scottish moorland and saw below them the Castle of Hermitage. The sentry on the battlements, alert for border raids, beat the alarm triangle. In a forecourt full of goats and chickens, children and cooking fires, the men buckled on their weapons and the women hurried their children to cover.

When the sentry recognized Bothwell he shouted down; the gates into the castle were opened and the party rode in. They were heavily travel-stained and very weary. Bothwell helped Mary to dismount. She was so stiff she could hardly stand and she leaned on him for a moment.

Bothwell said, 'Welcome to Hermitage, my sanctuary.'

'Thank you,' she said, trying not to sway.

'Are you all right?'

'Yes,' she said. 'Indeed I am. I am in good spirit.'

She moved from him and put a hand on Seton's shoulder.

'Come, let us go in.'

At that moment a woman appeared in the doorway at the head of the flight of stairs which led into the castle. She looked arrogantly down at the horses being led away and the fierce border women with their children who stared curiously at the heavily pregnant Queen of Scotland. Mary became aware of the woman. It was hate at first sight. Briefly they gazed at each other, then the woman dropped into a curtsy. As she did so Mary said to Bothwell, 'Who is that lady?'

Bothwell, aware of the hostility in Mary's tone, said carefully, 'She was the Lady Jean Gordon, your grace. The daughter of the richest of the highland lords.'

'Was?'

'She is now Lady Bothwell.'

Lady Jean had straightened up and she smiled. Any man worth his salt would have liked to have seen that smile when he woke and turned over.

'Welcome to Hermitage, your Majesty.'

Mary said sharply to Bothwell, 'Married? You are married?'

Bothwell replied discreetly, 'The border and the highlands are most happily joined.'

Mary forced herself to stand without Seton's help. She began to climb the steps. Pain seized her. She stifled a scream and began to collapse sideways. Seton rushed to hold her.

'Help me,' she said.

Bothwell strode forward and picked up Mary in his arms.

Mary with her face close to his gasped, 'I – gave – you – no permission – to – marry, my lord.'

And then everything was on the move to take her inside.

The castle was made for war not comfort. Its grey stone walls were, in places, eight feet thick; its windows slits. The main hall was stone flagged and without hangings on the granite walls. To warm it there was a huge stone fireplace where logs burned.

Three lean and matted hunting dogs sprawled in the heat of the fire. At the rough dining-table which filled a good part of the small hall sat Bothwell, Darnley and the Lady Jean. The remains of their food still lay on the table before them. Bothwell threw it to the dogs who snarled and would have fought had he not got up and kicked them apart. Darnley continued to drink as he had from the moment they had arrived. By now he had almost drunk himself sober. None of them spoke. Bothwell threw logs on the fire; the burning wood already there crashed and fell and as sparks flew out he stamped them into the stone floor to stop the rushes catching fire. The hall was full of wood smoke, the smell of grease from cooking and the tang of sweat on leather.

Suddenly one of the dogs stopped eating, pricked up its ears and began to whine and pace about. The others did the same. Darnley rose unsteadily and looked up at the gallery above them. Ballard stood there.

'Well?' said Bothwell impatiently, 'Well, man?'

Ballard said, 'By God's mercy, the long agony of the Queen in labour is over.'

The messenger rode four horses to exhaustion on his journey from Edinburgh. When he came into the choked and narrow streets of London he took a boat from the steps east of London Bridge as the tide was running out. It was dark when he passed the Isle of Dogs and landed at Greenwich. He ached from the journey. He was tired and afraid to go into the presence of the Queen. He stood on the landing stage with his back to the Palace and looked out at the great sweep of the river, and wished himself anywhere but there. He could hear music and laughter, for it was after supper and the Queen was dancing. The light of candles was in the windows. He found Cecil working.

From the rubies and emeralds in her hair to her gold

shoes Elizabeth glittered. Round her neck below the elaborate and beautifully worked lace of her ruff hung three ropes of pearls as big as fine grapes with a bloom on them. The dress itself, dark in colour, set off the dozens of huge rubies and emeralds sewn in intricate patterns with gold thread. She was leaping high in the air supported by Dudley who spun effortlessly to the lively music, when she saw Cecil. His grave appearance struck fear into her. As she came down she whispered in Dudley's ear and they stopped dancing. The musicians checked but she said, 'Play on, play on,' and they picked up the tune again and the other dancers continued to leap and revolve as she crossed to Cecil.

He spoke quietly in her ear. She did not reply. For a moment he stood perfectly still, then she turned as if she would return to Dudley and continue the dance. Her will failed her. She began to sink to her knees. The musicians faltered, the dance stopped, many of the dancers were in awkward, almost comic, positions. Elizabeth's head bowed almost to the ground. She crossed her arms tight over her stomach as if in agony. There was silence. She lifted her head and for the only time in her reign she was completely out of control in public.

She cried out, 'The Queen of Scotland is lighter of a fair son, and I am but barren stock.'

There was a gasp. A sort of sigh of sadness from the dancers through the room, and then ladies were hurrying to assist her to her feet and take her to the privacy of her bedroom. The other courtiers drifted away to spread the news through the court. Only Cecil and Dudley remained.

'There is worse news yet,' said Cecil. 'Bothwell has raised an army and the country has rallied to Mary. The whole land acclaims her because she now has borne a son. In Edinburgh alone they lit five hundred bonfires and celebrated day and night. I believe our friends may go down before her.'

'In that case, my lord,' replied Dudley, 'you and I can no longer afford to quarrel; for if they do and she comes South and raises the English Catholics our heads will look at each other from the top of pikes.'

'We must hope,' said Cecil, 'that James Stuart will find a way to deal with her.'

Among the duties of James Hepburn, Lord Bothwell, was that of Lieutenant of the Border. He was required to ride upon disobedient persons, invade them with fire and sword, besiege and cast down houses held against him. He might, in his sovereign's name, command assistance from neighbours under pain of death. The men who followed him had in their time fought the English, the French, each other and would, in fact, fight anybody for profit. They were veterans of the night raid: cut and run with the maximum plunder and the minimum loss of life. At sieges and full-dress battles they were not so happy, so Bothwell took them into the attack against Dunbar Castle at night.

In the Scottish tradition there were traitors in that castle who betrayed James Stuart and opened certain gates and portcullises. The borderers cut the throats of the sentries on the walls and then, using terror as a weapon, they lit torches, and shouting their war cries they swept through the castle from end to end. In the dawn they piled the dead in heaps in the courtyard and opened the main gates wide ready to welcome the Queen and her forces.

In the inner keep was a dried well. They dropped James Stuart twelve feet to the bottom, closed the grating over his head and left him to think of death.

At the same time Mary, dressed as a man in half armour with pistols at her belt, led her forces against the other lords who had murdered Riccio. Those she did not capture fled into England. Mary pursued them to the border and in her triumph she thought, it will not be long before I ride South and hunt them down in Elizabeth's court.

The cooking fires were burning in the courtyard and the borderers, having looted, ate. Bothwell, outside the gates, heard the faint sound and, turning his horse, galloped back into the castle to dismount at the keep. He pushed past the sentry and knelt at the grating.

He yelled, 'Stuart!'

'Aye.'

'Rouse yourself,' he jeered. 'Do you hear? It's your loving sister come to put a rope round your neck.'

James Stuart stood up slowly and listened – and he heard the pipes.

Mary, on a white horse, rode ahead of the pipers. On their flanks were the standard bearers; and behind them the main body of the army. Darnley commanded the rearguard following the gilded carriage which carried Seton and the royal baby. As Mary rode into the castle it was like the meeting of two fierce and barbaric tribes. The filthy and bloodstained borderers, many of them with food in their hands, cheered and fired pistols, waved their claymores and crowded to her. Her highlanders broke ranks to turn the piled bodies over to see if a ring or a chain or a dagger had been missed.

Bothwell fired a pistol into the air and shouted, 'The Queen has triumphed.'

The fighting men shouted themselves hoarse. Mary forced her way through the press to Bothwell's side.

'Where's my brother? Is he dead?'

'No. I've saved him for the scaffold.'

'Then let him say his prayers,' she said, 'and make his will for I shall hang him before the day is out. Bring me to him now so that I can tell him so.'

They removed the grating and dropped a rope to pull him up, and when he stood there dirty, dishevelled, his doublet unlaced, he looked a beaten man. But his voice was steady when he said, 'I had no part in the killing of Riccio.'

'Liar,' replied Mary.

109

Stuart suddenly got hold of the lining of his doublet and began to rip at it furiously so it tore away. Instinctively Bothwell moved between him and the Queen. From inside the ripped lining Stuart produced a document. Bothwell took it out of his hand. Stuart said calmly, 'It is a copy. The original is hidden safely in England.'

'Nothing will save you,' said Mary. 'I shall have your head for murder.'

'No,' said James, 'that is the bond and my name is not on it. But the first signature and therefore the first murderer, if you call it that, is your husband the King.'

'Stale news,' replied Mary, 'and I will deny it to all the world if I must.'

'Then read the last condition,' said Stuart. 'On the original it is written in the King's hand. Your good Harry would not sign without it.'

'What is it?' Mary asked Bothwell who was still reading.

'Riccio had to be killed in your presence, the King looking on, and then —'

She realized.

'My death,' she said.

'Yes.'

Mary thought, that is why Falconside tried to kill me. Harry wanted it. *He wanted it.*

James Stuart said, 'By God's grace the pistol would not fire, and then the noble Harry's courage failed him.'

'Now I see,' said Mary slowly, 'to punish you and the lords I must also punish the King.'

'No court,' said Stuart, 'will condemn us without him and even you' – his tone was sardonic – 'great and victorious Queen cannot act without the process of law.'

'Then, by God,' said Mary, 'I will act with it. It would give me joy to see you both on the same scaffold. I will do it now. Bothwell, arrest my husband.'

'Are you mad?' said Stuart quickly. 'Will you split the Kingdom and end the Stuart line? If you accuse brave

Harry out there then he will shout from the rooftops that your child is Riccio's bastard; that you were Riccio's whore; that the killing was the just execution of a commoner who committed high treason by cuckolding the King.'

Bothwell drew his dagger to kill Stuart.

'We do not need the law, madam, this gentleman died of his wounds in battle.'

Stuart backed against the wall, crouching as Bothwell moved to stab him.

Mary shouted, 'No! No! I forbid you.'

Bothwell stopped.

'For myself I care nothing,' she said bitterly. 'For the shame I care nothing. But I dare not give the heretics of England and Scotland a case against my son when I am dead.'

She was gasping and Bothwell was intrigued to see that her passion of hatred for her half-brother and the danger of the moment made her seem wanton and desirable.

'I will not hazard the inheritance of my son,' she said, 'even for the pleasure of Stuart's death.'

She left them.

'Ah,' said Stuart relieved, and sat with his back against the wall. 'Why is it that only in moments of great danger does she act wisely?'

The ambassadors of France, Spain and England came like the three wise men bearing gifts for the new-born child. They arrived at Dunbar that night and Mary received them most graciously in the only room not torn half to pieces by the looters.

'Madam,' said the English ambassador, 'my mistress is so joyful at the news of the birth of your fair son she pledges herself to be his godmother and she sends you this gift.'

It was a font. A massive font. All of gold. Of sufficient size to immerse the infant prince and of exquisite workmanship.

It was studded with precious stones so that the whole effect combined elegance with value. Those present applauded as the rich gift was uncovered and brought forward by the ambassador's attendants.

Mary turned to Seton and whispered, 'How it must have pained her to spend so much money.'

Seton, who was holding the infant James, giggled and had to turn her head away.

From Catherine de Medici there were three golden goblets set with jewels and presented on a golden tray; and from Philip's ambassador a beautiful and ornate case and inside it a jewelled cross with the figure of Christ upon it.

As the ambassadors stepped back Mary rose and took the child from Seton.

'My lords ambassadors,' she said, 'I thank you.'

The ambassadors prepared themselves for a long oration in praise of the generosity and wisdom of their respective monarchs. They were immediately jolted from the light trance into which they automatically relaxed.

Mary turned on her husband. Darnley had put by his golden armour and was preening himself in one of the many suits that Mary had bought for him when she was first in love with him. He chose to wear it in anticipation of appearing on the balcony at Mary's side when she would show the baby to her faithful warriors. The shock of her words to him was like a pistol shot in the room.

'My lord,' she said firmly, 'God has given you and me a son whose paternity is of none but you.'

Darnley could think of nothing better to do than to move to the child and kiss it.

Mary went on relentlessly, 'I protest to God and as I shall answer to Him at the great day of judgement, this is your son and no other man's son, and I'm desirous that all here, ambassadors, lords and ladies bear witness, for he is so much your son that I fear it may be the worse for him hereafter.'

Darnley tried to speak but Mary ignored him.

To the English ambassador she said, 'This is the prince, my lord, whom I hope will first unite the two kingdoms of England and Scotland. It bodes well that his godmother will be Elizabeth.'

The startled ambassador could only say, 'Why, madam, shall he succeed before your Majesty and his father?'

How could she explain? Stuart's revelation to her that morning had, at a stroke, changed her nature. She discovered she had in her the capacity to kill, not only judicially as monarchs must, but for revenge. She would gladly have killed her brother with her own hand and the sight of her husband so revolted her she wished him dead. From the moment when she realized that Falconside would have shot her through the belly killing both her and the child to please Darnley, the world had gone dark around her. It seemed to her that she had at last been debased to the standards of this country which she had hated from the moment she set foot in it. Her treacherous lords settled their affairs by murder. They could all, except Bothwell, be bought. To survive she must be more devious and bloody than they. How could she explain to the ambassador that the bright vision of her future which was intact only for that brief time in the ship between France and Scotland was now quite obliterated.

She said simply, 'Alas, his father has broken me.'

Darnley tried to brush it aside, appealing to the ambassadors over her head.

'Sweet madam,' he said, forcing himself to smile, 'is this your promise that you made to forgive and to forget all?'

She replied directly, 'I have forgiven all but I can never forget. What if the pistol had fired? What would have become of him and me?'

Darnley became desperate and said, 'Madam, these things are all in the past.'

'Then let them go,' she said, but the poor fool could never let anything go and he began to bluster.

'You would shame me before this company.'

'I would have this company know,' said Mary sharply, 'that you are this child's true father. That is all.'

'You shall hear more of this, madam. I shall have my rights of you.'

He almost ran from the room and the ambassadors itched to be in their own quarters writing their dispatches in order to get it absolutely word perfect.

They fired cannon on the battlements to salute her. They lit bonfires and it seemed to her looking down from the balcony into the courtyard that every man held a blazing torch in his hand. The child was passed to her and she held him up high over her head.

'Scotsmen,' she shouted, 'here is your future king. James VI of Scotland and in good time James I of England.'

The fighting men cheered. Her husband, trying to ride out of the castle and leave her, could not force his way through the press of men. Bothwell, also mounted, waited at the gate to stop him if he succeeded in reaching it. Mary was not finished with Darnley yet.

On the balcony she handed the child back to Seton and then raised both arms and the fighting men became silent.

'I am Queen by right of birth and by right of arms and tyranny I detest,' she said. 'I practise the old religion but tolerate the new. I rule in God's name and so I rule in justice and the better part of justice is mercy. Therefore on this great day of triumph I will be merciful and pardon James Stuart, Earl of Moray.'

As pre-arranged, the guards pushed Stuart into the courtyard. He was in a new suit of clothes. A groom brought his horse. He mounted. The soldiers parted for him as he paced his horse towards the centre of the courtyard. At the same time Bothwell began to ride to him from the gate. There was only one move left. Mary made it. She shouted, 'Before you all he shall be reconciled with both the King and Lord Bothwell!'

The soldiers, who had been deliberately blocking Darnley

according to orders now slapped the flank of his horse and drove him to join the other two men. When he was within reach, Bothwell immediately seized one of his hands as if in friendship. His other hand he extended to Stuart, who smiled, took it and reached with his free hand for Darnley's.

Darnley hissed viciously, 'I will not be reconciled with you, my lord, for you hate me.'

Bothwell replied softly, 'Not as much as he hates me. Put a good face on it so that the ambassadors and the baseborn are both deceived. It's all for policy's sake.'

Stuart crowded his horse closer and said, 'A man who first betrayed the Queen and then betrayed his fellow conspirators is like a leper and must be glad of a friend. And here I am.'

Darnley suddenly cheered up and took his hand.

'I shall wait,' he said, 'impatiently for the time when one of you will slit the throat of the other.'

'Or yours,' said Bothwell.

The borderers and highlanders were still cheering when Mary went in from the balcony. A member of the entourage of the English ambassador was waiting for her there.

'I have a private message for you,' he said quietly.

'Speak.'

'Not here.'

'Seton, bolt the door.'

As she did so Mary said, 'Now speak.'

'I am a servant of Thomas Howard, Duke of Norfolk, first peer of the realm in England. He is the leader of all the Catholic families and counts himself the loyal subject of Queen Mary Stuart.'

Seton gasped.

The man went on, 'He will prove it on the day she rides South to claim her throne.'

In the past Mary would have responded at once and generously but now all she said was, 'Go home to your master and tell him of my day of great triumph.'

When the man left she took the child in her arms and looked down at it.

'For your sake,' she said, 'murderers walk free and I must bear the company of your vile father for a little longer.'

CHAPTER NINE

All that Thomas Howard, Duke of Norfolk and Robert Dudley, Earl of Leicester had in common was the ambition to be a king. From the day Norfolk took it upon himself to challenge Dudley's right of entry to Elizabeth's bedchamber, and accuse him not only of kissing the Queen when not invited to do so, but of exceeding beyond all bounds his position at court, a certain constraint lay between them. Dudley, known to his enemies as the Gipsy, for his dark good looks, wild passions and skill with horses could fake docility when he chose. With the great Norfolk he was quiet as he waited the chance to destroy him.

The two men, sweating, went at each other with sword and dagger. If the points had not been buttoned both would have been cut in ten or twenty places. A pass ended and Elizabeth in the gallery above applauded them. It was she who had suggested that they should fence between games of tennis on the court at Hatfield. As she never did anything without a purpose, Cecil wondered if his spies had missed something at the recent christening of James which Norfolk attended.

Elizabeth was smiling. 'Bravo, Robin.'

Then she turned to Norfolk. 'You are short of breath, Thomas, from feasting and drinking in the Scottish court.'

The willowy Norfolk replied cheerfully, 'The christening of the Prince was a joyful affair as I told your Majesty.'

'And you favour that lady's hospitality, do you not, Thomas?'

Norfolk tried to maintain his light-hearted air, 'I did all that a good ambassador must do, your grace, but I confess the banqueting sits heavily on my stomach.'

Elizabeth came to the point.

'At all times of the year birds fly South from Scotland to nest in the roofs of my palaces. One such whispered that the Duke of Norfolk longs for the Queen of Scotland to be widowed again so that he may marry her.'

Norfolk panicked. 'What?' he said. 'What lies are these. I love to sleep upon a safe pillow. My only ambition is to serve you.'

Dudley's moment had come. He tapped Norfolk lightly on the shoulder with his rapier.

He said in a jeering voice, 'Come, come, my lord, you are far too modest.'

Norfolk controlled his anger. He was aware of the dark figure of Cecil on the balcony beside the Queen. He said with his voice shaking, 'I am not nor ever shall be a suitor to Queen Mary.'

Dudley took two goblets of wine from a side table and offered him one.

'Excellent,' he said. 'Then I give you a toast. To the Lord Bothwell whom rumour has it is bedding the lewd lady at this moment.'

Norfolk lost all reason. He whipped his rapier through the air to smash the button from the point on the table's edge and then lunged at Dudley. Dudley snatched his rapier and dagger from the table and immediately they were fighting in earnest. The fight moved the whole length of the court. Dudley, aware of the unbuttoned point, retreated steadily looking for the opportunity to disarm Norfolk.

Elizabeth, deeply concerned for Dudley, ran down from the gallery.

'Stop!' she shouted. 'Stop! I command you. Stop!'

Cecil, terrified for her safety, shouted for guards and the guards came running along the gallery and down the stairs with their pikes levelled. Dudley was now cornered and Norfolk was poised for the death thrust when a guard running full tilt came between them driving his pike into the wall beyond Norfolk, the butt running across his chest making a barrier. There was a panting pause. Elizabeth reached them. Norfolk looked at her white face and terrible eyes and dreaded her judgement.

She said softly, 'I see that you would kill my loyal subject to defend the honour of my enemy.'

Norfolk gasped distractedly, 'The slander was against me. This lord tried to disgrace me in your eyes. I challenge him to the death.'

Elizabeth said, 'There will be no deaths here. Only in Scotland.'

She had not meant to say so much. Her tone was lighter when she said, 'I am happy you are loyal only to me for I hear that Mary Stuart has changed, and poor treacherous Darnley walks in darkness, his enemies all around him.'

Cecil was limping towards her as fast as he could move. She was laughing again and apparently light-hearted as if the incident had never happened.

'Here he comes,' she said, 'my very spirit.'

Then as she took Cecil's arm and he felt her shaking, she looked back at Norfolk and said, 'Stay in the light, Thomas.'

There was a high wind blowing. The long gallery which led to the royal apartment in the Castle at Edinburgh was empty. There were strange shadows from the guttering lights on the wall and in the distance could be heard the banging of doors which had been left half-open. Along this gallery came a drunken and hysterical figure. He had his arm round the shoulders of a whore who half supported him. He was shouting.

'Where are you? Where are you? Mary, Mary, where are you? Where is the Queen?'

He came to the door of the outer room of the royal apartments and pushed it open to smash against the wall. The room was bare and stripped of its hangings. He went through it and into another room and this too was empty. He was running back into the gallery where he had left the whore when he was faced by an ominous figure, sword in hand, and he stopped in shock. It was only a guard.

'Where's the Queen?'

'At Holyrood.'

This sobered him.

'Holyrood?' he said. 'But she was here. She rode here. She lived here in triumph. She raised her flag over the Castle. She came to show the world that she had as much power as her mother before her. She stood where Mary of Guise died. She was here. Why has she gone?'

The guard said stolidly, 'She is at Holyrood.'

'She would not go there,' said Darnley. 'It is a place of murder.'

The guard said patiently, 'Her Majesty has gone to Holyrood Palace.'

'You are a good fellow,' said Darnley. 'Here is your reward.'

He shoved the whore at him.

In the turret room Mary rose abruptly from an uneaten supper and said, 'I will divorce him.'

Ballard and Bothwell also rose to follow her into the presence chamber.

Ballard said, 'Divorce casts doubt upon the paternity of the child.'

'Then I will have the Pope annul the marriage.'

'The issue of an annulled marriage is declared illegitimate.'

'What must I do to be rid of him?'

'There is no way,' said Ballard stubbornly.

'In exile,' remarked Bothwell, 'are those Scottish lords whom you would not pardon.'

'No,' said Ballard at once taking the point, 'that is murder.'

'I do not understand,' said Mary.

Bothwell ignored the priest. 'Madam, in this land any lord may challenge another who has insulted, offended or betrayed him. The matter is settled by duel of honour. Pardon those lords and bring them home. It will not be murder.'

The door of the presence chamber slammed open and Darnley stood there.

'I've had enough,' he shouted. 'Everywhere I go I am shunned. People look through me like a ghost. I will not be made to feel guilty any more over a scrap of paper.'

'Go to your bed,' said Mary. 'You are drunk.'

'No. I will go to your bed. Either that or I leave the kingdom.'

'Then do so,' said Mary.

Darnley began to laugh.

'Yes I will. I will travel. I will go to Italy. I will have audience with the Pope. He will annul this false marriage. You were so anxious to have me, sweet wife, that you did not wait for the dispensation which cousins must have to marry.'

'Annulment will make your son a bastard,' said Bothwell.

'I know. I know,' jeered Darnley, 'and she will do anything to save her son's inheritance. So come to bed, sweet wife.'

Bothwell moved violently towards Darnley but Mary stopped him. She knew exactly what to do.

'Go,' she said. 'Both of you.'

As they went Darnley strutted to the bedroom door and opened it.

'For God's sake, smile,' he exclaimed. 'And bring me some wine.'

Before she went to the wine Mary touched the ring on her finger. Riccio had given it to her after Darnley broke in on them.

He had said before she put it on, 'It acts quickly. Let me show you.'

He pressed the small catch and lifted the stone of the ring to show the grey powder in the container underneath.

Mary's hands were steady as she poured the two glasses of wine and then added the powder to one of them. When she went into the bedroom Darnley had removed his doublet and boots and was sprawling on the bed. She gave him one glass and drank the other.

'I drink to your great potency, my lord,' she said.

He drank down his wine and laughed at her. He began to fondle her.

'Even if I disgust you,' he said, 'you will love and caress me and have me by your side again as King. As I mount you, so shall I mount the throne again.'

'My poor boy,' she said, 'you are frightened and you do not disgust me.'

Her fingers stroked him as she slowly undressed him. His wet lips parted as he submitted to her. His eyes closed. She murmured, 'You are tired. There, my poor boy, you are tired. Rest. Close your eyes. Come I will lie beside you on the bed. Let me calm you before we make love. Lie down. Lie down.'

It was simple for her until he realized, drunken and drugged as he was, that something strange was happening to him and he said, 'This is a trick. This – is – a – trick. You – have —'

'No,' said Mary, 'you are quite safe with me. You have nothing to fear. Sleep. Go to sleep. Go to sleep.'

'I don't – want —'

'Sleep,' said Mary. 'Sleep.'

When he was completely unconscious she eased herself away from him and stood up. At that moment the secret door in the panelling opened and Bothwell was there.

'Have you killed him?'

'No.'

'I came to do you that service.'

'He is drugged.'

'He is diseased.'

Mary did not immediately understand.

'Diseased?'

'Since before the birth of the prince he has been vagabonding at night. He is blatant with everything he does. He has the French disease. He has been to a doctor. He is poxed. He will rot with it. There is no hope for him.'

'Oh merciful God,' said Mary. 'Then I am spared more than I knew.'

Suddenly she began to weep passionately. Her long-pent-up emotions burst out and she seemed about to faint. Bothwell stepped forward to support her. She clung to him with all her strength and he kissed her. She did not resist. Roughly he pulled away from her, and took the drugged Darnley by the heels and dragged him into the turret room, then he came back to Mary and took her again in his arms. This time she resisted. She put her hands against his chest and tried to push him away. Her resistance excited him. He seized her dress and ripped it to the waist. She began to fight back, raking at him with her nails. She sobbed and screamed. They went down on the bed and he tore more of her dress off. He began to kiss her passionately. His weight on top of her held her down and no matter how hard she twisted her head from side to side she could not get away from him. She sobbed bitterly but his strength and passion overwhelmed her and in the next hours he released a wantonness in her nature which had been as hidden from her as her capacity for vengeance before the events at Dunbar. Long afterwards she thought how closely they were linked, these two passions, and how they overwhelmed all judgement, reason and honour.

Darnley woke slowly to the full light of day. His head ached so much he could barely raise it. He realized eventually that the bedchamber was stripped of hangings, cupboards, presses, clothes-horses, candelabra, even the canopy and the bedding were gone. He lay on the flat wooden board of the bed. There was a vile taste in his mouth and it was all he could do to drag himself into the turret room to look for water. It was bare. He almost ran to the presence chamber. It too was empty except for one thing. A sheet of paper was pinned to the far door by Darnley's own dagger. He crossed the room in a panic. He pulled the dagger out and forced himself to read the paper.

> *Husband, there are certain lords in England who have been punished enough. Ruthven, Falconside, Douglas and Morton are therefore pardoned by the mercy of their Queen. Soon you shall meet them again.*

Darnley said softly, 'I am betrayed.'

He pulled open the door to the rest of the palace and there stood two guards. Just beyond them was the Lord James Stuart in black armour, reminiscent of Ruthven at the murder of Riccio. He slammed the door and ran stupidly back a few paces into the room, then he dropped to his knees, laid back his head like a dog baying at the moon and howled on a long dying note, 'I am betrayed.'

The letter fell from his fingers and lay on the blood stain on the floor where Riccio had died with Darnley's dagger in his throat.

On the last part of the journey they tied the dying Ruthven to his saddle. He sat there bolt upright in his black armour determined to live until he reached Scottish soil. He succeeded by a mile, and his companions were deeply impressed when he told them with his last breath that he could see flights of angels waiting to lead him into Heaven.

Bothwell said, 'So he's dead at last. Is Riccio running before him in Hell crying for mercy I wonder?'

'Do you insult him?' said Stuart icily. 'Do you even insult the dead?'

'The dead,' said Bothwell, 'are so much meat.'

It was the following night and they were walking together to meet the returned lords.

In a low vaulted room in Edinburgh Castle the dead body of Ruthven was laid out in his black armour on a rough table lit by candles.

'We have brought him home to lie in Scottish soil,' said Falconside emotionally. 'Over his dead body we have sworn vengeance so let us now decide who will kill the King in combat.'

'The King is sick of the pox,' said Bothwell. 'He cowers in bed and he will not fight.'

'Then we will drag him out,' said Morton, 'and kill him as he did Riccio.'

'No one,' said Bothwell patiently, 'cared about the death of a little foreigner. Everyone will care about the murder of a King.'

They glared at each other across the body.

'I thought you, above all, wanted him dead, my lord.'

'Oh I do,' agreed Bothwell. 'But not —'

Stuart interrupted, 'As you know, his Majesty has a house outside the walls of Edinburgh where he took his whores and young men.'

'So?' said Bothwell.

'And there,' said Stuart, 'he plans to murder Mary Stuart.'

Bothwell began to laugh. 'He hasn't the strength or will to kill a cat.'

'He has filled,' said Stuart ignoring him, 'the cellars of Kirk o' Fields with gunpowder. It is part of a plot. Darnley is in league with Catherine de Medici who also hates the Queen. It is a Catholic plot planned in Paris. He means to lure the Queen to Kirk o' Fields, make his excuses to leave her for some hours and then —'

Bothwell was almost helpless with laughter.

'Blow her up? When he has the choice of knife, gun, poison, rope, he chooses gunpowder? Nobody, Jamie, would choose gunpowder in these hard times. It costs too much.'

'Nevertheless,' said Stuart deliberately, 'the cellars are full of gunpowder.'

Bothwell stopped laughing.

Stuart went on, 'His Majesty is a notorious drunkard and a fool. Also, as you say, he is sick. I think he will bungle his attempt on the Queen's life and blow himself up instead.'

'So,' said Bothwell, 'the innocent Queen must find a way to persuade the wicked King to travel to the house at Kirk o' Fields.'

Even Morton smiled.

'Can you help us?' said Stuart.

Bothwell looked at the dead body in its armour.

'Bury your dead,' he said, 'and leave the rest to me.'

He went.

When he was sure he could not be overheard Falconside said, 'And next he will lord it over us.'

'No,' said Stuart. 'He lacks the proper caution.'

The baby prince James was taken to Stirling Castle and put in the care of the Erskine family. With a heavy heart Mary left him there. In this time of her personal rule she knew she must always be ready to act quickly. She dared not leave the young prince exposed to possible kidnapping. Her own journey to France at the age of three had been for the same reason: to keep her safe while her mother ruled.

With her guard she came late at night to Bothwell's castle.

When he greeted her he said, 'She has gone.'

He had fulfilled his promise to send his wife away.

Now I am committed, she thought, now I would go with him to the world's end. They lay together in the same room where she had given birth to James. Their lovemaking was so passionate, so prolonged and abandoned that she almost fainted with it. Afterwards she said, 'I adore you beyond all reason and I hate the woman you have married. I loathe the thought of you with her.'

'I am not with her.'

'For the first time in my life I am loved and fulfilled and I will not share you.'

'That marriage,' he said, 'was a business arrangement.'

Mary remembered the smouldering Lady Jean and bit into his shoulder, 'Is that true?'

Bothwell laughed in the darkness and lifted her head away by the hair. 'There is an oath that a borderer must swear to prove himself guiltless. By Heaven above and Hell beneath, by his part of paradise, by all that God made in six days and seven nights, and by God Himself. Thus do I swear.'

'When I am away,' she said, 'I can think of nothing but you. When you are not in my bed I dream of you. I want you for ever. I love you with all my heart.'

She tried to see his expression in the moonlight through the window but he turned his head from her. In her jealousy she said angrily, 'I will have her divorce you.'

'And then?' he said.

'When the King has been called to account by those he betrayed you will see.'

Bothwell realized that he could be the King. Not a puppet king, not a regent, but the King.

'What shall I see?'

'Already you have my honour and my life,' said Mary

126

passionately, 'and I risk my soul even for Father Ballard will no longer confess me.'

He said mockingly, 'Even the flames of Hell.'

'Don't,' she said furiously.

He touched her and she clung to him. 'The choice is mine,' she said, 'but I cannot repent of you and return to the Church. I have turned my back on God for you. Now do you believe the strength of my love?'

'Oh yes,' he said, 'I believe that. But what shall I see?'

She took him by the hair with both hands and lay over him. She said, with her lips close to his ear, 'I will give you what I most treasure on earth. My kingdom.'

He deliberately rolled from under her and got out of bed.

'What is it?' she said.

He was silent.

'Why are you silent? Do you fear your wife and the Gordons, is that it? I'm a match for that lady as you should know. Are you craven or is it shame? Have you used me?'

He was still silent.

'If you value my love and all that has passed between us, then answer me.'

'You have offered me the Crown.'

'Yes.'

'I will be no puppet king. I will be the master.'

Mary got out of bed and went to him and pressed her naked body against his.

'I'd glory in that,' she said.

He put his arms round her. Then she told him the one thing she had kept from him.

'I carry your child under my heart, and I will boast of it to the world in good time.'

'By God,' he shouted, 'a son. A prince. Now we must be resolute if we are to be free to marry.'

'I will do anything you ask,' she said.

In his sickroom in Glasgow Darnley was asleep and dreaming

of evil things and groaning under them. The beautiful young god was quite changed; his beard greasy, his face covered with sores and his breath so foul that Mary was as far away from him as she could sit. On the table before her was a candle, ink, quills and a sander. Three pages of the letter which she was still writing were to one side, and the silver casket with its key in the lock to the other. She was very troubled as she wrote to Bothwell.

He would not agree to travel except with condition that I promise to be with him at bed and board as man and wife when he is cured in Edinburgh. To make him trust me I pretended that it should be so. Alas, it troubles me to lie so well and to deceive and betray. For he was most humble and trusting in his speech to me when I came here. I long to sleep as all around me sleep but since I cannot as I desire, that is in your arms my dear love, I will write more. I subject myself altogether to your will. Whatever shall be the outcome I will obey you. That he is condemned to death by the pox which is the wrath of God upon his vile nature I do believe with all my heart. So what is planned is no sin. God forgive me if I do wrong. God prosper you my only love and hope and grant that soon this unhappy burden is taken from us and we are man and wife.

She signed the letter and sanded it and called softly, 'Andrew. Andrew.'

Bothwell's page had been sleeping on the floor wrapped in his cloak. He was guarding the door. He woke at once with a dagger in his hand.

'All is well,' she said.

She put the letter in the casket and locked it and gave it to him.

'Take this to your lord. We shall travel early tomorrow.'

Andrew took it and went. The click of the door jerked Darnley awake and he cried out, 'Help me. Help me.'

His debauched face was white as lard and sweating. He put out his hands towards Mary.

'What is it?' he said, 'who is there?'

'I am here,' she said, 'your loving wife. Don't be afraid.'

The poor diseased creature blurted out. 'Forgive me. Forgive me,' and began to weep bitterly.

And Mary wept too for she was now so far in there was no way out.

They travelled the next morning on the road from Glasgow to Edinburgh. It was a bright day and Mary's spirits were lifted as she rode ahead of the horse-drawn litter. They were some miles from Edinburgh and approaching a hump-back bridge when over it appeared horsemen. Darnley, hearing the hooves, looked out from the litter. He was horrified to see, riding towards them, Bothwell, James Stuart, Morton, Falconside, Douglas and Huntly. They surrounded the litter. As one man they dismounted. Then knelt in the dust, very humbly, and removed their hats.

'We welcome your return, your Majesty,' said Bothwell.

'All past things are buried and over, your grace,' said Stuart.

And the brutal Morton said, 'We wish you well in health again, sire.'

Darnley believed them. He called out to Mary, 'Now all will be well. I thank you. I thank you.'

They remounted. Bothwell close to the litter said, 'Your grace, the doctor has asked a time of quarantine before you re-enter Edinburgh.'

'So be it,' replied Darnley cheerfully.

'I have had your house at Kirk o' Fields prepared for you. Will you go there?'

For a moment Darnley was uneasy. He looked at the faces of the men on the horses. Then he said to Mary, 'Will you stay with me at Kirk o' Fields, madam?'

'Yes, Harry.'

'Then I am content, Mary.'

The house stood between the old falling walls of two churches and near an almshouse for beggars. Its approach was by an alley named Thieves Row. On the ground floor a bedroom was furnished for the Queen. In the room above it one of the fine beds which Mary of Guise had imported from France many years before was prepared for Darnley. Carpets and tapestries which had previously hung in the royal apartments at Holyrood furnished the poor house.

The respectful lords escorted their King to his house, wished him a quick return to health and rode on into Edinburgh to wait.

On that February night the frosty air seemed to make the stars bigger and more glittering than Andrew could remember. The cold, the excitement and the anticipation so affected his bladder that he twice had to relieve himself behind a bush in sight of the lighted window from which he could hear the Queen's voice singing.

He could still hear her voice faintly from the cellar as he lifted a barrel of gunpowder from the top of a pile ready to lay a fuse. It slipped from his hands and fell with what seemed to him to be an enormous crash and he stopped, sweating, to cock his head towards the low ceiling. The voice still sang. He picked up the barrel again and worked his way backwards towards the cellar steps; then up and out onto the path at the end of the house laying a thick trail of black powder. He nearly screamed when a heavy hand thumped onto his shoulder.

'Good boy,' said Morton, 'Good boy. This way – under the trees for cover when she blows.'

In Thieves Row Bothwell waited with Seton. They, too, could hear the Queen as she sang. This time she accompanied herself on a guitar.

From the trees Morton whistled. In the lane Bothwell said to Seton, 'Now, mistress.'

In the bedroom Darnley said petulantly, 'Why do you keep Davie's guitar, and why do you play it? Is it to anger me once more?'

'No, Harry,' replied Mary. 'No. It was my hope to soothe you so that you would sleep well.'

There was a knock on the door and Seton entered. She spoke directly to Mary.

'Your grace, it is time to leave.'

'What?' said Darnley. 'You promised to stay.'

'There is a marriage-feast of two of my dear servants in Edinburgh,' replied Mary.

'Margaret Cawood,' said Seton, 'and the musician Sebastien, my lord.'

'I must go,' said Mary, 'for form's sake, but I will return soon. I will take the guitar with me since it offends you.'

She hesitated in the doorway. 'It is just a year since Davie died,' she said.

He heard the sound of their horses going away. Then there were other sounds he could not understand. He got out of bed but he was very weak and could hardly walk. He dragged himself to the window. Dark figures moved across the garden and out of sight at the end of the house. Now he knew how Riccio had felt that fatal night. He moved as fast as he could to the door of the bedroom and tried it. It was locked on the outside. He snuffed the candles in the room. Then he went to the window and tried to open it. At first it wouldn't budge and then at last it opened outwards.

The lords who had just arrived watched Morton strike a flame and put it to the long trail of powder. In the bedroom Darnley was sobbing as he tied his sheets together. His lust for life overcame his weakness. He pushed the heavy bed close to the window and tied the end sheets to the foot of it. He scrambled over the windowsill to dangle in the darkness until he braced his feet against the side of the house. The cold of the bitter night struck through the shift which was all he wore. The sheets were not long enough and he hung whimpering, then he dropped. Stones cut his feet but he felt nothing. Like an animal he emptied his bladder for flight and it froze on him. He picked himself up and ran from the house into the darkness.

The flame sped down the ten steps into the cellar and across the floor. In Edinburgh they thought the magazine of the castle had blown up, so violent was the explosion.

Andrew, sheltering behind a tree felt every hair on his head stand up straight.

The blast caught Darnley, picked him up and hurled him through the air. He landed face down and the soft earth dented to his shape. He dug with his fingers to drag himself forward. Inch by inch by inch he moved. No bones were broken in his body but the blast had so smashed him that he could move no faster than a snail. Behind him in the crater where the house had stood were small flickering fires. He knew he must reach the wall at the end of the garden and get over it. He came to it. His strength was almost gone. He turned himself over and sat with his back against it. Then he saw them coming for him. Dark shapes stumbling from the far side of the crater. He screamed out, 'For the love of Jesu Christ who died for us all, spare me, spare me.'

They were glad of his voice to guide them.

When they got to him they saw he was stark naked. The blast had ripped the shift off him.

The room of the wedding reception was empty except for Mary and Bothwell. Bride, groom and guests all rushed outside after the first shock of the explosion. Mary could hear their excited voices. She looked at Bothwell. He poured brandy and put her hand round the glass.

'Drink!'

'He was to be challenged to a duel,' she said stupidly. 'To have an honourable death. You told me so.'

Could she really have believed it, thought Bothwell. She knew he could barely crawl.

'Death is death, however it comes,' he said. 'We must now look to our future.'

Beggars from the almshouse were the first to approach the ruins from which smoke was still rising. They saw something on the far side of the crater. One of them, bolder than the rest, advanced on the naked corpse. He knelt, he saw the cord tight round the neck.

'Murder! Murder! Murder!'

It was a shout to echo down the centuries.

CHAPTER TEN

Catherine de Medici, who loved food, sat up in bed guzzling a meal. She roared with laughter and nearly choked when the embarrassed Scottish ambassador told her how the wicked Darnley had tried to blow up Mary and bungled it.

King Philip of Spain working in his windowless study where candles burned day and night was too busy to look up as he listened to the news from Scotland. Having, some years before, murdered his own idiot son, what startled him was the crass method. When the ambassador was silent the austere monarch stopped writing for a moment and murmured that in his experience God solaced the bereaved in good time.

At the Palace of Whitehall, things were done differently. Elizabeth was in black, all her ladies were in black as were Leicester and Cecil. The canopy of the throne was black. The walls of the presence chamber were draped with black. The Scottish ambassador, dressed in his finest, entered, faltered – then advanced miserably and bowed. Clearly this was not going to be his day. Cecil in a funereal voice announced him and the two who followed.

'The ambassadors of France, Spain and Scotland, your Majesty.'

'We are in mourning,' said Elizabeth harshly, 'for the late King Henry of Scotland. We mourn him because the Scottish court does not. He was once our subject. We are shocked at his abominable murder. We are astounded at what followed. The King was taken at dead of night and buried without ceremony. His clothes, his armour, his goods and his horse were given to the Lord Bothwell. Voices cry out that Bothwell is the murderer. The Scots have risen in rebellion. Protestant, Catholic, lord and peasant have combined to destroy the tyrant *and yet Queen Mary Stuart has married him.*'

There was a faint murmur of well-drilled dismay from all the ladies. Elizabeth turned her entire attention to the Spanish and French ambassadors.

'It was once said in Catholic courts that Elizabeth would marry her horsemaster who murdered his wife. Her subjects would then turn her out in favour of Mary.'

At that moment both the Spanish and French ambassadors would gladly have hanged Bothwell with their own hands. Elizabeth went on, 'I have not married. Leicester is innocent, my people did not rebel and Mary Stuart does not rule here.'

She spoke the last words with immense relish and then she smiled her most dazzling smile and moved to Dudley and put her hand on his arm.

'Tell your masters,' she said, 'do not interfere in Scotland and nor will I. Let the Scottish Queen settle her own affairs as I once settled mine.'

And she left in triumph on Dudley's arm. As they all bowed the sober gentleman at Cecil's elbow said, 'How she longs to hear of Mary's death.'

'And how she dreads it,' said Cecil.

The man at his elbow was Sir Francis Walsingham.

*   *   *

Mary married Bothwell in dark secrecy. She forced through his divorce in a few days. Then, because no priest would join them, and no foreign ambassador or Scottish lord support them, they were married at four in the morning by Protestant rites while Edinburgh slept. They fled to Bothwell's castle to await his forces from the border and she made love on their wedding night more in despair than passion.

Darnley cried out to her and she woke violently. In the instant Bothwell was awake beside her, a dagger in his hand from the sheath at the bed head.

'What is it?'

'A dream.'

'A dream,' he grunted. 'Be thankful it's not James Stuart knocking on the door.'

'I am full of fear, waking and sleeping.'

Bothwell, not understanding the reason said, 'All my forces will be here by dawn. It's three days since I sent the messengers.'

Mary replied, 'I do not fear my brother and his army.'

'Come,' said Bothwell and began to embrace her. She neither responded nor pushed him away. As he kissed her throat she said, 'I am guilty of murder.'

He drew back.

'Yes,' she said, 'my husband's murder. That is why all Scotland is up in arms and I am loathed.'

He took her firmly by the shoulders.

'You are not. I am. It means nothing to me. He was worthless, so I used you to put him in a trap. You are innocent.'

'I wished him dead.'

'But not murdered. You knew nothing until it was over.'

'That is true. Thank God, I knew nothing of it for if I had I might still have done it because I love you more than life and honour.'

He was touched by this.

'When we ride out of here tomorrow,' he said, 'to crush

this rebellion, I want you to look the world in the eye without guilt or regret. Say to yourself, I, Mary Stuart, Queen of Scotland and the Isles, had no part in the murder of Henry Darnley.'

She shook her head.

He said, 'For love of me, will you do that?'

She touched his face. She kissed him.

'For the love of you,' she said, 'what have I not done for the love of you?'

As they began to make love there was the raw clanging of the alarm triangle and they broke apart. Mary was fearful, but Bothwell was very cheerful.

'It's all right, it's my borderers. It's nearly dawn.'

He laughed at her and kissed her palm.

'Later, he said, 'we must get up now.'

The room was in a tower and Mary, still uneasy, went to one of the slit windows. She gasped at what she saw and exclaimed, 'Jamie!'

He rushed to join her then to the window on the other side. As far as he could see on either side mailed horsemen were advancing. When they heard the alarm they lit torches to show their power and their contempt for the defenders. Bothwell ran to buckle on his sword belt.

'We can hold them off until my men come.'

Outside Stuart bellowed in triumph. 'Bothwell! Show yourself. Are you afraid?'

'Stay here,' said Bothwell and he ran up to the top of the tower and onto the battlements. He was panting as he got to the parapet. He looked right and left for archers before he stepped up onto it.

'I'm here.'

'Tell her Majesty to come down to us. We have no quarrel with her,' bellowed Stuart. 'It is you we have come for.'

Mary heard him as she came out onto the battlements behind Bothwell and she said fiercely, 'I will not go down.'

She ran to the parapet before Bothwell could stop her.

She looked down at the upturned bearded faces of the flower of her nobility.

'This time when I have won,' she shouted, 'I will crucify you brother on the gates of this castle and hang every lord who rides with you from the walls.'

Ignoring her Stuart said, 'Bothwell, have you the courage for single combat or will you go on hiding in the skirts of the Queen? I'm not a sick man like the King you murdered.'

'I will cut him to pieces,' said Bothwell and turned at once to go down and arm.

Mary clung to him. 'I forbid you to fight.'

'I will not be shamed, Mary.'

'You shall not risk yourself.'

Stuart's voice bellowed up. 'It's your only hope Bothwell. Look down!'

Mary ran again to the parapet. Below they led a horse into the light of the torches, and on its back were tied three naked men. Each had his throat slit.

'You're finished, here are your messengers,' shouted Stuart. 'Now will you fight?'

'That I will.'

He ran down to the bedroom shouting, 'Andrew! Andrew! My armour! Bring my armour.'

Stuart took a pull at a flask and said to Morton, 'When he comes down we shall both cut his throat. It's a cheaper way in than a siege.'

'Amen to that,' said Morton.

Mary said desperately to Bothwell, 'You must not. They will kill you as they did Davie.'

He paid no attention. He was concentrating on the straps, his sword, his dagger, his half-armour.

'I will fight,' he said. 'He dare not go back on a challenge before the rest of them. I will finish it this time. But when I go down you must take the secret way out of here. Andrew will guide you.'

'No,' she said. 'We must go together. I beg you.'

'I will not be dishonoured,' he said.

As in every crisis she knew what to do and it made her calm. She went to him and kissed his face; he pushed her away impatiently.

'My dear love,' she said, 'he knew you would never refuse a challenge. You are no match for the treachery of these times. Who remembers the honour of the dead?'

She went quietly out of the room and then she slammed the door and barred it from outside.

Inside, Bothwell rushed to it and tried the handle but he did not smash at the door. It was too heavy for him to break down.

He said, keeping his voice down for fear that he would be heard through the slit windows. 'I beg you do not disgrace me, Mary.'

Through the door she said. 'I carry your child in my body. Your death will be mine. You must escape. Rouse the borderers yourself. I am still the Queen. While I live I reign.'

'Mary, do not do this,' he said urgently.

'Goodbye, my sweet love. Go now.'

Then she shouted, 'Seton! Seton!'

Seton who was terrified and had been hiding came slowly to join her.

'Dear Mary Seton,' she said, 'give me courage. Come with me and look down on those traitors because soon we must open the gates and give ourselves up to them.'

'God help us,' said Seton and crossed herself.

When they came out onto the battlements the first light was in the sky. She looked down at Stuart and shouted, 'I shall watch him kill you from here brother.'

Her voice was quite steady. She prayed silently that Bothwell had gone.

'You shall not have long to wait,' she shouted, 'for my husband is determined and I cannot dissuade him.'

In the bedchamber a section of the wall stood open. The room was empty.

The lords brought Mary captive back to Holyrood Palace through a mob that screamed and jeered and threw filth at her.

'Burn the whore,' they shouted. 'Adulteress. Murderer.'

And they tried to rip the clothes off her. The escort had to beat them off with swords and pike butts. By the time they got her into Holyrood she had been awake and under extreme pressure for thirty-six hours. She was on the edge of madness.

Outside the mob howled for her. In the presence chamber Stuart said, 'See how much the people hate you.'

He held up a document the lawyers had drawn up.

'Here is the instrument of abdication. Sign it.'

'I will never abdicate,' she gasped, 'I am the Queen. I will die the Queen.'

'Huntly,' shouted Stuart, 'Huntly!'

The door from the turret chamber opened and Huntly entered. He carried the silver casket. Mary saw it at once.

'Now will you sign?' said Stuart.

'How did you get it?' she demanded.

'Your letters to Bothwell prove you are a murderess and you led the King to his death.'

'No,' she screamed. 'I am innocent. I am Mary Stuart, Queen of Scotland and the Isles and I am innocent.'

'Sign or I will publish them and try you.'

'No, no, no, no.'

Stuart said, 'You are beyond hope. Bothwell will not be coming to your aid, lady, because I have him.'

Mary shook her head from side to side and intoned, 'Not true. Not true.'

'Tomorrow,' said Stuart shaking her, '*I shall hang him!*'

'No,' she screamed and went over the edge of reason. She ripped at her clothes and then ran to the window to try to throw herself out. The lords seized her and she collapsed. Her last memory was of Stuart holding the abdication document and Huntly the casket.

She woke slowly. First she was aware of a single candle burning. Then of the wooden boards under her and a blanket over her. Then of the raw pain in her belly. She turned her head to focus on the man who dozed on a stool beside the bed.

'Father,' she whispered.

He woke.

'Drink,' he said and he held a cup to her lips.

As she moved to take it the pain stabbed her and she gasped.

'You have miscarried of twins,' he said, 'and lain senseless for two days.'

'Two days?' she said in anguish. 'Oh God, he is dead and I have lost his children.'

In her weakness and despair the tears ran down her cheeks.

'Did he send any message to me?'

Ballard said stonily, 'I am forbidden to speak of it. I stayed only to nurse you. Now you live so I shall leave you.'

'No, please,' begged Mary.

He was implacable. 'You have betrayed God and the Church in this land.'

'Confess me.'

'Do you repent?' he said reluctantly.

'I do most bitterly repent if I have betrayed God in this land.'

'But do you repent,' he insisted, 'of your false marriage to the Lord Bothwell?'

Slowly she shook her head.

'No.'

He rose.

'Then pray that God in His great mercy will show you your error. For I may not hear your confession.'

The door opened and James Stuart entered.

'Leave us, priest.'

Ballard left.

Stuart stood over her. 'Will you sign the instrument of abdication?'

'Never,' she whispered.

He turned his back on her and went to the other door and opened it. There, dirty, bearded and tattered, stood Bothwell. She whispered, 'Jamie.' And then she sobbed, 'Jamie.'

She was too ill to rise but he ran to her and held her and they kissed. She clung to him.

'I thought you were dead. They told me.'

He looked round. Stuart had gone.

'Your brother saw an advantage in keeping me alive. They will pardon me and spare you if I persuade you to abdicate.'

She shook her head. 'I cannot. I cannot.'

'Listen,' he said urgently, 'Elizabeth is raging against your imprisonment. She has sent such arrogant demands for your release that Stuart cannot much longer stop the rest of them executing you. I fear what can happen to you. Your brother wants you out of the way alive before it's too late.'

'No,' wept Mary. 'He wants me dead too.'

'Above all,' said Bothwell insistently, 'he is a Stuart. He'll save you if he can. But he can only do it if you abdicate.'

'And you?' she said clinging to him.

'Exile.'

There was the sound of the door. Bothwell said almost cheerfully, 'There's no hope in the grave, Mary.'

Stuart in the doorway said, 'Make your decision – there is no more time.'

Stuart brought her to the border.

'I bid you farewell,' he said formally, 'we shall not meet again.'

'So you must hope.'

'Long life, sister. We will bring your son up a Protestant.'

He turned and spurred away.

'My son,' said Mary to Seton. 'My son, God help him.'

'But you are alive, madam – and free.'

Free, thought Mary. With sudden exuberance she put her horse to the gallop. She was laughing and the wind was in her hair.

She shouted out loud, 'Free! Free!'

And Seton remembered that she was only twenty-five years old.

CHAPTER ELEVEN

It was early summer, full of birdsong, when Elizabeth went on one of her progresses. Between one great English house and the next she turned aside with Dudley and let it be known, to the well-concealed amusement of her court, that she wished for an afternoon of privacy to consider certain matters of State in the company of the Earl of Leicester.

An hour later as they rode in thick woodland she said, 'The Catholics of the North have flocked to pay her homage since she came over the border. At Carlisle she held court even. Is she mad to act so blatantly when she is in my hands?'

In an attempt to soothe her suspicions Leicester said, 'She has never learned discretion.'

'I wonder. Perhaps I have misread her all these years. Perhaps her rash behaviour hides some devious purpose. Well it is said I have a wolf by the ears. Let us look at the animal.'

The two Queens met in a clearing where the trees stood

so thick they were like a wall and their branches almost shut out the sky.

Elizabeth's heart beat fast and she could not get her breath as she observed Mary's eyes and mouth and hands and the grace of her movement. She found her more beautiful than she could bear, and was bitterly jealous. At last she said, 'Well, cousin, I am here to meet you as you demanded so urgently.'

Mary, thinking only of herself, immediately plunged in.

'Dear sister and cousin, my business can only be discussed between us face to face. I know you to be the enemy of all rebels against their Prince.'

'That is true,' replied Elizabeth.

'The crime of my people against their anointed Queen is so great it buries all past differences between us. I am confident of your help. I ask it as a right.'

Cautiously Elizabeth said, 'I see that you have courage,' and waited for the bargaining to begin.

It was inconceivable that Mary meant her words to be taken as anything but a polite opening move.

'And I see that you are the great Queen of whom all speak,' replied Mary confidently.

'And you are young,' said Elizabeth politely.

'Not too young to ride at the head of an army.'

Now we begin, thought Elizabeth.

'You've come to ask me for an army?'

Encouraged, Mary said, 'An army, supplies and money.'

'And money,' echoed Elizabeth incredulously.

'Which I shall most happily repay to you when I reign once again in Scotland,' replied Mary promptly.

I begin to believe, thought Elizabeth, that she is blind to her position and the consequences of her past deeds.

Mary saw her smile.

'And how else can I aid you?' asked Elizabeth warmly. 'Be open with me, dear cousin, for believe me there is no waking hour in my day when you are far from my thoughts.

Your fate is linked with mine. We are princes. We are joined by blood. What else have you to tell me or to ask from me?'

Now, thought Elizabeth, now is the time. Make me your offer if you have one.

Mary said, 'Nothing.'

'Nothing?' Elizabeth seemed surprised.

'What else could there be?'

Elizabeth put it delicately, 'Some helpful word concerning the murder of Lord Darnley.'

Mary had expunged the past from her mind. She was mildly surprised that Elizabeth mentioned it.

She said as a formality, 'Of course, rest assured that I am innocent in the matter,' and waited to hear when her army would be ready.

Elizabeth put the key into the lock of the prison door.

'That gives me great joy for when you are honourably acquitted of the crime of which you are accused by the people of Scotland you shall have your army and your money.'

Mary was amazed and could hardly believe her.

'Madam,' she said, 'put it out of your mind that I came to England to save my life. I came to recover my honour and if you doubt my word that I am innocent then I will go at once to France.'

'You shall not,' said Elizabeth, closing the prison door.

Mary lost her temper. 'Your grace, in the past you have sheltered those very traitors who now rule in Scotland. They move freely into England for shelter and just as freely they return. Do you offer me less than my treacherous subjects?'

Elizabeth did not reply and Mary, becoming more angry, went on, 'Am I your prisoner? If so, by what law? And if you forbid me to go to France what will you do with me?'

'I will,' said Elizabeth turning the key, 'take you deeper into England for your protection.'

Mary was stunned. Never in history had one monarch

imprisoned another who was a guest in the land *and* in time of peace.

'If you are innocent,' said Elizabeth, 'what have you to fear?'

'You have deceived me,' cried out Mary. 'You are in league with my brother. I will answer no accusations. Who is there who may try me? Who is my equal? Will you do it?'

Then she lost her head completely and shouted, 'No, you lack the courage. You hope to dishonour me but it is you who are dishonoured.'

On the edge of the clearing Dudley shifted uneasily in the saddle and waited for Elizabeth to explode. Instead she spoke quietly.

'Did you believe that I would send you to Scotland at the head of a great army full of my Catholic nobles? Did you believe that I would sacrifice my reputation on your account *when you offer me nothing in return?* It is not enough, madam,' she went on bitingly, 'to speak one's mind in season and out as you do. That is not the conduct of a Queen. It is the outpouring of a pampered woman demanding that all indulge her. It does not surprise me that you are here, helpless, and your brother rules. You are not fit for the high office to which you were born.'

Provoked beyond reason Mary poured out her true feelings.

'And you, madam, who hate me and wish me dead and fear to kill me, you are my mortal enemy. I have noted since the day when you denied me a passport through England all the blows you have struck against me. I glory in your hatred for it is clear to me that Elizabeth the bastard, usurper and heretic is cursed by God and will soon be too old to bear a child and will die a solitary old woman. Above all, it is clear that Elizabeth fears Mary and whatever my fate my son will rule here in time.'

The iron control that had carried Elizabeth through all

the perils of her early life and through all the diplomacy of her realm did not desert her in the face of these deadly insults.

She said, 'You have noted all the blows I struck against you?'

'All,' replied Mary.

'All but one,' said Elizabeth. 'It was I who sent Henry, Lord Darnley to your court on a white horse, sweet cousin.'

As she heard these words Mary knew them to be true. She was crushed to silence by the malevolence and subtlety of the woman before her.

'Any queen,' said Elizabeth scornfully, 'who could be gulled by such a pretty wicked fellow and take him to her bed and put a crown upon his head does not inspire fear. She inspires pity. You have my pity, madam, as you had it on the day I sent Darnley North knowing you to be without discretion, wisdom, or any of the attributes of a queen. I hoped to have dealings with you but I see that since that time you have learned nothing. It is not surprising that you are now spoken of in the courts of Europe as an infamous royal whore.'

Mary raised her riding crop to strike Elizabeth and as she did so Elizabeth's horse shied and reared and it was all that Elizabeth could do to control it. By the time she had done so, Leicester had galloped between them seizing the bridle of Mary's horse.

Mary shouted at him, 'My lord, I urge you to guard your mistress well for there are many who would see her dead.'

And wrenching the bridle from his hands she turned her horse round and galloped back to her guards and then away.

Elizabeth did not look after her. She stroked the neck of her mount and listened to the sounds of the wood all round them. Finally she said, 'Now I have no choice. I must keep her locked up until the day of her death.'

*　　　*　　　*

The secret war began. Its focus was Mary in captivity to be freed and Elizabeth on the throne to be murdered.

Urged by Norfolk the Catholics of the North raised their banners and marched South to the glory of the Catholic God to free Mary their Queen. Elizabeth's army marched North to the glory of the Protestant God and smashed them. Then the executions began. Hundreds hung by their necks and putrefied. Their mothers and widows wept.

Next came Ridolfi: like Riccio before him a Papal agent; but unlike him full of absurd confidence and self-delusion. It was he who nailed the Papal bull excommunicating Elizabeth to the Bishop of London's house in St Paul's Churchyard. It was the formal declaration of the secret war. From that moment English Catholics were damned if they obeyed the Queen's laws, and traitors if they obeyed the Pope. The long-disused scaffold on Tower Hill was re-built and Norfolk died on it betrayed by Ridolfi.

The Pope's secret army in this time of plot and counter-plot, was that great body of English priests who were trained in France for martyrdom then infiltrated into England.

Among them was Ballard.

Mary was at Chartley. Her room was spacious and reminiscent of the presence chamber at Holyrood. After so many years it no longer irked her. She was free to hunt, to receive visitors, to write and receive letters. But day and night she was watched.

When her door opened without warning and a dashingly dressed military man entered, Mary turned away thinking it was yet one more arrogant courtier sent by Walsingham or Cecil to question her. Seton ostentatiously lit the candles in the alcove with its crucifix and prie-dieu, also keeping her back to him.

Without removing his plumed hat the man barked,

'Madam, I am an English officer from the French court. Captain Fortescue.'

Mary opened a book and pretended to read. The officer continued, 'I bring you greetings and some letters which I must tell you I've already shown the authorities here for I am a loyal Englishman.'

'Give them to my servant,' said Mary turning a page.

'No,' he said arrogantly, 'I am ordered to wait for a reply.'

To the soldier at the door he said, 'Leave us.'

As it closed and Seton moved reluctantly to take the letter he spoke again. This time in his old voice without the harsh tone of authority which he had used from the moment he entered.

'Waste no time on those, your grace.'

Her heart leapt and she ran to him and kissed his hand.

Sharp as ever Ballard said, 'Up, up, your grace. There's work to do. You,' he said to Seton, 'put an ear to the door and give us warning.'

He took a second letter from his riding boot.

'This is from Philip in Spain,' he said. 'I will take him your reply and then return to England. There will be no more failures. She will die, and the Spanish fleet will land the Spanish army from the Netherlands. At the same time the Catholics will rise here and rescue you.'

'How soon?'

'Read the letter, your grace.'

'At once,' she said, but after a moment she stopped and hesitantly touched his arm. 'Father,' she said, 'forgive me, but do you know any news of the Lord Bothwell?'

'Bothwell,' said Ballard, 'has died insane in a Danish prison.'

'Insane.'

She turned to the corner set aside for prayer and knelt.

'Oh God,' she said, 'now do I repent of all my actions

that have brought him to such a terrible end. Oh, God forgive me.'

Ballard touched her shoulder.

'Then I will hear your confession at last, my sovereign lady.'

'Yes, Father,' she said. 'It is time.'

With Ballard at the centre the plot began. Walsingham and Cecil intercepted the correspondence to and from Mary and broke the code.

The danger was so great for Elizabeth that Cecil, not waiting for the plot to come to its climax, went to her and demanded that now, after all these years, she should have Mary tried and executed. Elizabeth took to her bed to avoid a decision but he came again the next day.

'No,' she said. 'I am ill. I am too ill to decide.'

He said grimly, 'You are the Queen. Above all, you must defend your loyal subjects.'

He put a list of names before her. She read: Babbington, Tilney, Abington, Barnwell, Charnock, Windsor – and then looked up in horror.

'All these?' she said. 'I have been kind to them.'

'All have sworn to kill you.'

'Oh, Jesu.'

'All are of your household – but they will kill you for that viper whom you will not kill.'

She said bitterly, 'I am excommunicated as was Henry my father – these young men are Catholics and so it is no sin to kill me.'

'Madam,' said Cecil acidly, 'it is the act of a saint. Now will you protect your true subjects by destroying your enemies?'

'All who associate with that lady,' said Elizabeth with hatred, remembering how bravely Norfolk died under the axe, 'come early to the grave.'

'Destroy her.'

'No,' shouted Elizabeth. 'I cannot.'

'If I bring you proof that she insists on your death?'

Elizabeth wavered.

'Written proof,' said Cecil driving to win, 'irrefutable proof?'

Elizabeth said softly, 'Beyond all doubt. To hold up before Parliament and people.'

'Beyond all doubt,' he said.

Again she faltered and he prayed for the right answer to convince her.

She said, 'Is there such proof?'

'There will be,' he said. 'I promise you.'

'No forgeries, William,' she said, 'no false confessions from torture. It must be in her own hand.'

He left before she could change her mind.

As the door closed Elizabeth thought, it was always from the beginning her death or mine.

On the day the letter was intercepted from Mary in which she personally endorsed the assassination of Elizabeth, the arrests began. They took Ballard first, brought him to the Tower, stripped him and hung him by his wrists from rings set high in the walls so that his feet hung clear of the ground. There they left him in torment until his trial. The rest they brought to the Tower in batches as they found them. Fourteen English gentlemen came to trial with Ballard, to be hanged, drawn and quartered.

Mary, in high spirits at the thought of her deliverance and the Spanish invasion, was induced by her keeper to go hunting. For three hours her rooms were searched. They smashed every cupboard, chest, drawer and floorboard. They found sixty different cyphers, and fourteen years of secret correspondence in support of the Catholic cause against Elizabeth. Cecil was exultant.

When Mary returned he was reading a list of English noblemen. He glanced up and said, 'Madam, you cast an evil spell on all you meet.'

They were packing everything in the room including her few jewels and some coin.

'Leave me that,' she commanded.

'No.'

'My servants must be paid. Is Elizabeth so poor she must steal it?'

'Leave it,' said Cecil.

'And now, my lord?'

On the following day after supper in the Palace of Whitehall, Cecil came to Elizabeth and begged her to accompany him into the council chamber. She was in low spirits and reluctantly went with him. When she entered she saw the table piled high with the letters taken from Mary's room. Walsingham approached her and bowed and gave her the fatal letter in which Mary endorsed her death. He and Cecil stood perfectly still while she read it. She put it carefully on the table.

'In my reign,' she said, 'I have pardoned many rebels and winked at many treasons. No matter the evidence I fear a terrible retribution if I sign a death warrant.'

They were still silent.

'Where will you send her?'

'Fotheringay Castle,' said Cecil.

'Jesu, to that evil place?'

Inexorably Cecil said, 'I have brought you the proof positive.'

Elizabeth suddenly let out an angry cry and swept all the evidence from the table to the floor. Papers flew everywhere with the violence of it.

She shouted, 'If she begs forgiveness of me she shall live.'

When she entered the grim hall she said, 'Am I to be murdered here?'

The officer did not reply. As they parted her from

Seton, Mary kissed her warmly and said, 'Be of good cheer. I'm very happy now it has come to it.'

When they closed the door behind her she saw that the room had a single barred window. A chair with its high back to her faced the window. There was a sound of keys as the door was locked. It was cold and she shivered. She limped across the room to try to see out from the window. And then she became aware of someone and gasped and turned. Elizabeth was sitting in the chair. In the years since they had first met they had both aged beyond their years with suffering. Each saw it in the face of the other.

Elizabeth said, 'As you see I am not dead.'

'Forgive me,' said Mary, 'but I must sit.'

She moved to do so in one of the few other chairs.

'The bitter winters of my imprisonment and the damp that runs down English walls have entered my bones.'

'My council,' said Elizabeth, 'my Parliament, my people demand that I bring you to trial.'

'Will you permit me the sword when the time comes and spare me the dull axe?'

'Do not joke with me about death,' said Elizabeth savagely. 'From the day of your imprisonment I have lived in constant fear of assassination. Your followers, madam, your assassins, your plotters. I have forced myself to walk in the open freely among my people and I've never known at which moment the dagger or the pistol would do its work. So make no jokes with me about death.'

'I am very tired,' said Mary. 'Tell me what you want and then go.'

She should be on her knees, thought Elizabeth, and found it hard to go on. But she forced herself to speak.

'I want to spare you, but I cannot unless you renounce your claim to my throne, send no more murderers and beg my forgiveness in writing.'

'I knew of the plans for your death,' said Mary without hesitation, 'I was glad of them. But now in this room as I look at you face to face it's another matter. I'm happy that you've been spared and I will be happy to ask your forgiveness personally here between these four walls.'

'That is not enough, write it.'

'No, because it would damn me for ever in the eyes of posterity.'

'I will keep the letter quite secret from all save my chief minister. I offer you your life.'

This struck fire into Mary and she said, 'I long for the trial. I long to stand before the world after these years of darkness and defend myself. I thank God that in His mercy and wisdom He has brought me to it. I shall die a martyr to the Catholic faith which is the true and eternal faith. Nothing will prevent it. No man is my judge, not even you may judge me, madam, now. Only God.'

'How little you have changed,' said Elizabeth. 'How wildly you rush to your destruction.'

She went to a small table which stood shadowed in the corner. On it was something covered by a dark cloth. She removed the cloth and held up the object. It was the casket. She took out a handful of letters.

'Your letters to Bothwell,' she said with repugnance. 'Madam, will you be seen a noble Catholic martyr when these are read to the court. What will the world think when, after the details of the plots to kill me are revealed, we turn to the past. Your life is steeped in blood and violence. The actions which led to your disgusting marriage to the murderer Bothwell will be fully recounted before the court and before the world. Your absurd love letters will be read out for the people to gloat upon. Will all this evidence of treachery, cruelty, murder and lust rise like a hymn of praise to God? Or will it cast you down for ever?'

Mary relived the moment of her capture by Stuart and the first time that she had been confronted with the silver casket. She was almost engulfed by panic.

'Oh God,' she said, 'Oh God.'

Elizabeth pressed her advantage.

'Write one short page to me and you will be spared the trial and you will live. For the first time in your life put from you your personal desires and behave like a Queen.'

'No,' said Mary.

She forced herself to walk across to the silver casket, to touch it, to look at the letters in Elizabeth's hand so that she might know she could face any revelation that would be made at her trial.

'You cannot tempt me,' she said. 'You are the Devil and I will not succumb to you. In all my early years I was misled and betrayed. I sinned most grievously and suffered most bitterly. I lost my faith. I will deny nothing to you here in this room for I have repented of it all. I have made my peace with God. I begged to atone for all that has gone before and God has brought me here to die in glory. I have been greatly punished. My kingdom, my possessions, my husband, my child, all have been taken from me and I have been shut away for many years in abject misery and now I must die. It is my destiny.'

She looked into Elizabeth's eyes.

'And it is your destiny, Elizabeth, to kill me. You cannot evade it. I shall leave to you the pomp, the power, the intrigue and all that a prince in this world must endure or may enjoy. Nothing you can say or do will avoid my martyrdom. So now it is I who pity you for you must order the thing you have always feared more than death itself. The judicial murder of an anointed Queen. It will torment you to the end of your days.'

Elizabeth went to the door and banged on it.

Dudley opened it.

'My lord,' said Mary, 'I will pray for your mistress at the moment of my death.'

He was touched by this and he went to her, knelt and kissed her hand. Elizabeth, standing in the doorway, looked at her ageing lover at the feet of her eternal rival.

'Madam,' she said, 'if your head had matched your heart I would have been the one waiting for death.'

CHAPTER TWELVE

All night as she prayed she heard the sound of the carpenters at work in the great hall. In the morning the scaffold was ready. It had rails round it and was covered in black. On it stood a low stool and a long fur cushion – and a block also covered with black. To the right and left were seats for the Earl of Shrewsbury and Kent. Against the far wall stood the executioner and his assistant, each in black, wearing a mask, and with a white apron round his waist. Spectators packed the hall from end to end and were held back by a long rank of pikemen to leave a path along which Mary would walk to the scaffold.

When they came for her she was calm. It was Seton who wept. Mary embraced her and said, 'Do not weep. I am happy. I am truly happy. Farewell, Mary, you were ever faithful to me and I thank you. So pray for me.'

On the scaffold she raised her voice triumphantly, 'I freely forgive all my enemies and all who have lusted after my blood – for in my end is my beginning.'

She loosed her dark cloak and it fell. The spectators gasped to see that she was dressed all in scarlet. She knelt upon the cushion and placed her neck on the block. The headsman raised his axe. She spread her arms wide and cried out.

'Into thy hands, Oh Lord, I commend my spirit.'

The axe fell.

MARGARET IRWIN

Margaret Irwin's novels of the Sixteenth and Seventeenth Centuries have been popular for over three decades. She blends exciting adventure, romance and penetrating character-study with scrupulous historical accuracy.

YOUNG BESS 35p
With the death of Henry VIII, the young Elizabeth stands second in succession to the throne. She must use any weapon to fight a world of ruthless enemies to defend her right to the throne.

ELIZABETH, CAPTIVE PRINCESS 35p
Imprisoned in the Tower, consoled only by Robin Dudley, Elizabeth found herself a pawn in a ruthless game of politics where the wrong move meant death . . .

ELIZABETH AND THE PRINCE OF SPAIN 35p
Unwilling bridegroom to Mary Tudor, Philip of Spain found himself more and more fascinated by the warmth and vitality of her younger sister.

THE PROUD SERVANT 35p
The story of James Graham, Marquis of Montrose, the soldier-poet who fought so magnificently and so fruitlessly for his King, Charles I.

THE BRIDE 30p
The story of the romance between the Marquis of Montrose and the enchanting, wayward Princess Louise, sister of Rupert of the Rhine.

ROYAL FLUSH 35p
The story of Minette, sister of Charles II of England and wife of Philip, Duke of Orleans, who was the brother of Louis XIV of France.

THE GAY GALLIARD 35p
The ever controversial story of Mary, Queen of Scots and of Bothwell, her lover.

JEAN PLAIDY

'One of England's foremost historical novelists'—

BIRMINGHAM MAIL.

The persecution of witches and puritans in the 16th and 17th centuries
DAUGHTER OF SATAN　　　　　　　　　30p

The story of Mary Stuart
ROYAL ROAD TO FOTHERINGAY　　　　30p
THE CAPTIVE QUEEN OF SCOTS　　　　35p

The infamous Borgia family
LIGHT ON LUCREZIA　　　　　　　　　30p

Life and loves of Charles II
THE WANDERING PRINCE　　　　　　　30p
A HEALTH UNTO HIS MAJESTY　　　　30p
HERE LIES OUR SOVEREIGN LORD　　　30p

Catherine de Medici
MADAME SERPENT　　　　　　　　　　30p
THE ITALIAN WOMAN　　　　　　　　30p
QUEEN JEZEBEL　　　　　　　　　　　30p

Robert Carr and the Countess of Essex
THE MURDER IN THE TOWER　　　　　30p

The Tudor Novels
THE SPANISH BRIDEGROOM　　　　　　30p
GAY LORD ROBERT　　　　　　　　　30p
THE THISTLE AND THE ROSE　　　　　30p
MURDER MOST ROYAL　　　　　　　　35p
ST. THOMAS'S EVE　　　　　　　　　30p
THE SIXTH WIFE　　　　　　　　　　30p

REGENCY ROMANCES
BY GEORGETTE HEYER

THE UNKNOWN AJAX   35p
'A dazzling performance, perhaps the best of all her Regency
novels . . . as full of delicate contrivance as a Jane Austen
tale'—THE BIRMINGHAM MAIL.

FARO'S DAUGHTER   25p
BEAUVALLET   25p
THE CORINTHIAN   25p
APRIL LADY   30p
BLACK SHEEP   30p
SYLVESTER   30p
COUSIN KATE   30p
BATH TANGLE   30p
FREDERICA   30p
ARABELLA   30p
SPRIG MUSLIN   30p
THE MASQUERADERS   30p
THE TALISMAN RING   30p
THE CONVENIENT MARRIAGE   30p
THE TOLL-GATE   30p
THE QUIET GENTLEMAN   30p
THE BLACK MOTH   30p
DEVIL'S CUB   30p
ROYAL ESCAPE   30p
VENETIA   30p
REGENCY BUCK   35p
THESE OLD SHADES   35p

These and other PAN Books are obtainable from all book-
sellers and newsagents. If you have any difficulty please send
purchase price plus 5p postage to P.O. Box 11, Falmouth,
Cornwall.
While every effort is made to keep prices low, it is sometimes
necessary to increase prices at short notice. PAN Books re-
serve the right to show new retail prices on covers which
may differ from those advertised in the text or elsewhere.